Answer Manual to Accompany

INTRODUCTORY LINEAR ALGEBRA

WITH

APPLICATIONS

THIRD EDITION

Bernard Kolman
Drexel University

prepared by

JAMES BROOKS

Macmillan Publishing Company
New York
Collier Macmillan Publishers
London

Earlier editions, entitled Introductory Linear Algebra with Applications copyright © 1976 and 1980 by Bernard Kolman.

Macmillan Publishing Company
866 Third Avenue, New York, New York 10022

Collier Macmillan Canada, Inc.

ISBN: 0-02-366030-9

Printing: 1 2 3 4 5 6 7 8   Year: 4 5 6 7 8 9 0 1 2 3

CHAPTER 1

Section 1.1, page 9

2. $x = 1$, $y = 2$, $z = -2$.

4. No solution.

6. $x = 13 + 10z$, $y = -8 - 8z$, $z =$ any real number.

8. No solution.

10. $x = 2$, $y = -1$.

12. No solution.

14. $x = -1$, $y = 2$, $z = -2$.

16. 1.5 tons of regular and 2.5 tons of special plastic.

18. 20 tons of 2-minute developer and a total of 40 tons of 6-minute and 9-minute developer.

T.1. The same numbers s_j satisfy the system when the pth equation is written in place of the qth equation and vice versa.

T.2. If $s_1, s_2, \cdots, s_n$ is a solution to (2), then the ith equation of (2) is satisfied: $a_{i1}s_1 + a_{i2}s_2 + \cdots + a_{in}s_n = b_i$. Then for any $r \neq 0$, $ra_{i1}s_1 + ra_{i2}s_2 + \cdots + ra_{in}s_n = rb_i$. Hence $s_1, s_2, \cdots, s_n$ is a solution to the new system. Conversely, for any solution $s_1', s_2', \cdots, s_n'$ to the new system, $ra_{i1}s_1' + \cdots + ra_{in}s_n' = rb_i$, and dividing both sides by nonzero r we see that $s_1', \cdots, s_n'$ must be a solution to the original linear system.

T.3. If $s_1, s_2, \cdots, s_n$ is a solution to (2), then the pth and qth equations are satisfied:

$$a_{p1}s_1 + \cdots + a_{pn}s_n = b_p$$
$$a_{q1}s_1 + \cdots + a_{qn}s_n = b_q.$$

Thus, for any real number r,

$$(a_{p1} + ra_{q1})s_1 + \cdots + (a_{pn} + ra_{qn})s_n = b_p + rb_q$$

and so $s_1, \cdots, s_n$ is a solution to the new system. Conversely, any solution to the new system is also a solution to the original system (2).

2. (a) $\begin{bmatrix} 5 & -5 & 8 \\ 4 & 2 & 9 \\ 5 & 3 & 4 \end{bmatrix}$; (b) $AB = \begin{bmatrix} 14 & 8 \\ 16 & 9 \end{bmatrix}$; $BA = \begin{bmatrix} 1 & 2 & 3 \\ 4 & 5 & 10 \\ 7 & 8 & 17 \end{bmatrix}$;

(c) $\begin{bmatrix} 18 & -19 \\ -2 & -1 \end{bmatrix}$; (d) impossible; (e) $\begin{bmatrix} -2 & 17 \\ 16 & 31 \end{bmatrix}$;

(f) $\begin{bmatrix} 6 & 12 & 18 \\ 12 & 6 & 24 \end{bmatrix}$.

4. (a) impossible; (b) impossible; (c) impossible;

(d) $\begin{bmatrix} 5 & 1 & 9 \\ 18 & 15 & 40 \end{bmatrix}$; (e) $\begin{bmatrix} -28 & 35 \\ 14 & 21 \end{bmatrix}$; (f) impossible.

6. (a) $\begin{bmatrix} 29 & 12 \\ 4 & -1 \\ 34 & 21 \end{bmatrix}$; (b) $\begin{bmatrix} 7 & 17 \\ 2 & 13 \\ 13 & 37 \end{bmatrix}$; (c) $\begin{bmatrix} 18 & 40 \\ 28 & 34 \\ 20 & 24 \end{bmatrix}$;

(d) impossible; (e) $\begin{bmatrix} 34 & 8 & 44 \\ 26 & 6 & 34 \end{bmatrix}$; (f) impossible.

8. $a = 3$, $b = 1$, $c = 8$, $d = -2$.

10. $AB = \begin{bmatrix} -4 & 7 \\ 0 & 5 \end{bmatrix}$; $BA = \begin{bmatrix} -1 & 2 \\ 9 & 2 \end{bmatrix}$.

12. (a) $\begin{bmatrix} 2 & 0 & 0 & 1 \\ 3 & 2 & 3 & 0 \\ 2 & 3 & -4 & 0 \\ 1 & 0 & 3 & 0 \end{bmatrix}$; (b) $\begin{bmatrix} 2 & 0 & 0 & 1 \\ 3 & 2 & 3 & 0 \\ 2 & 3 & -4 & 0 \\ 1 & 0 & 3 & 0 \end{bmatrix} \begin{bmatrix} x \\ y \\ z \\ w \end{bmatrix} = \begin{bmatrix} 7 \\ -2 \\ 3 \\ 5 \end{bmatrix}$;

(c) $\left[\begin{array}{cccc|c} 2 & 0 & 0 & 1 & 7 \\ 3 & 2 & 3 & 0 & -2 \\ 2 & 3 & -4 & 0 & 3 \\ 1 & 0 & 3 & 0 & 5 \end{array}\right]$.

14. $\begin{aligned} 2x \quad\quad - 4z &= 3 \\ y + 2z &= 5 \\ x + 3y + 4z &= -1 \end{aligned}$.

16. (a) $\begin{bmatrix} 6 \\ 25 \\ 10 \\ 25 \end{bmatrix}$, (b) $\begin{bmatrix} 12 \\ 11 \\ 17 \\ 20 \end{bmatrix}$.

18. AB tells the total cost of producing each kind of product in
    each city:

    $$\begin{array}{cc} \text{Salt Lake City} & \text{Chicago} \end{array}$$
    $$\begin{bmatrix} 38 & 44 \\ 67 & 78 \end{bmatrix} \begin{array}{l} \text{Chair} \\ \text{Table} \end{array}.$$

20. (a) 2800g,   (b) 6000g

T.1.   Let $A = [a_{ij}]$ be $m \times p$ and $B = [b_{ij}]$ be $p \times n$.

   (a) Let the ith row of A consist entirely of zeros, so
       $a_{ik} = 0$ for $k = 1,2,\cdots,p$. Then the (i,j) entry in AB is

       $$\sum_{k=1}^{p} a_{ik}b_{kj} = 0 \text{ for } j = 1,2,\cdots,n.$$

   (b) Let the jth column of B consist entirely of zeros, so
       $b_{kj} = 0$ for $k = 1,2,\cdots,p$. Then again the (i,j) entry of
       AB is 0 for $i = 1,2,\cdots,m$.

T.2.   Let A and B each be diagonal $n \times n$ matrices. Let $C = A + B$,
       $c_{ij} = a_{ij} + b_{ij}$. For $i \neq j$, a_{ij} and b_{ij} are each 0, so
       $c_{ij} = 0$. Thus C is diagonal.
          Next let $C = AB$,

       $$c_{ij} = \sum_{k=1}^{n} a_{ik}b_{kj} \qquad\qquad (*)$$

       For $i \neq j$, and any value of k, either $k \neq i$ and so $a_{ik} = 0$, or
       $k \neq j$ and so $b_{kj} = 0$. Thus each term in the summation $(*)$
       equals 0, and so also $c_{ij} = 0$.   This holds for
       every i,j such that $i \neq j$, so C is a diagonal matrix.

T.3.   Following the notation in the solution T.2. above, if A and B
       are scalar matrices, then $C = A + B$ is scalar with $c_{ii} = c$
       $= a + b = a_{ii} + b_{ii}$ and $C = AB$ is scalar with $c_{ii} = c = a \cdot b$
       $= a_{ii} \cdot b_{ii}$.

T.4.   (a) Let $A = [a_{ij}]$ and $B = [b_{ij}]$ be upper triangular matrices,
           and let $C = A + B$. Then for $i > j$, $c_{ij} = a_{ij} + b_{ij}$
           $= 0 + 0 = 0$, and thus, C is upper triangular.
              Next let $C = AB$, $c_{ij} = \sum a_{ik}b_{kj}$. If $i > j$, then for
           each k, either $k > j$ (and so $b_{kj} = 0$), or else $k \leq j < i$
           (and so $a_{ik} = 0$). Thus $c_{ij} = 0$.
       (b) Proof similar to that for (a).

T.5. The jth column of **AB** is

$$\begin{bmatrix} \sum\limits_{k} a_{1k}b_{kj} \\[6pt] \sum\limits_{k} a_{2k}b_{kj} \\ \vdots \\ \sum\limits_{k} a_{mk}b_{kj} \end{bmatrix}$$

T.6. The i,ith element of the matrix product AA^T is

$$\sum_{k=1}^{n} a_{ik}a_{ki}^{T} \;=\; \sum_{k=1}^{n} a_{ik}a_{ik} \;=\; \sum_{k=1}^{n} (a_{ik})^{2} \,.$$

Thus if $AA^T = 0$, then each sum of squares $\sum\limits_{k=1}^{n} (a_{ik})^{2}$ equals

zero, which implies $a_{ik} = 0$ for each i and k. Thus A = 0.

T.7.

(i) $\sum\limits_{i=1}^{n} (r_i+s_i)a_i = (r_1+s_1)a_1 + (r_2+s_2)a_2 + \cdots + (r_n+s_n)a_n$

$= r_1 a_1 + s_1 a_1 + r_2 a_2 + s_2 a_2 + \cdots + r_n a_n + s_n a_n$

$= (r_1 a_1 + r_2 a_2 + \cdots + r_n a_n) + (s_1 a_1 + s_2 a_2 + \cdots + s_n a_n)$

$= \sum\limits_{i=1}^{n} r_i a_i + \sum\limits_{i=1}^{n} s_i a_i \;,$

(ii) $\sum\limits_{i=1}^{n} c(r_i a_i) = cr_1 a_1 + cr_2 a_2 + \cdots + cr_n a_n$

$= c(r_1 a_1 + r_2 a_2 + \cdots + r_n a_n) \;=\; c \sum\limits_{i=1}^{n} r_i a_i \,.$

T.8. $\sum\limits_{i=1}^{n} \sum\limits_{j=1}^{m} a_{ij} = (a_{11} + a_{12} + \cdots + a_{1m}) + (a_{21} + a_{22} + \cdots + a_{2m})$

$+ \cdots + (a_{n1} + a_{n2} + \cdots + a_{nm})$

$= (a_{11} + a_{21} + \cdots + a_{n1}) + (a_{12} + a_{22} + \cdots + a_{n2})$

$+ \cdots + (a_{1m} + a_{2m} + \cdots + a_{nm})$

$= \sum\limits_{j=1}^{m} \sum\limits_{i=1}^{n} a_{ij} \,.$

2. $A(BC) = \begin{bmatrix} -2 & 34 \\ 24 & -9 \end{bmatrix}$.

4. $r(sA) = \begin{bmatrix} -48 & -24 \\ -12 & 36 \end{bmatrix}$, $(r+s)A = \begin{bmatrix} 16 & 8 \\ 4 & -12 \end{bmatrix}$,

$r(A+B) = \begin{bmatrix} 24 & 24 \\ -18 & 0 \end{bmatrix}$.

6. $(A+B)^T = \begin{bmatrix} 5 & 0 \\ 5 & 2 \\ 1 & 2 \end{bmatrix}$, $(rA)^T = \begin{bmatrix} -4 & -8 \\ -12 & -4 \\ -8 & 12 \end{bmatrix}$.

12. (a) $\begin{bmatrix} -3 & -2 \\ 4 & 1 \end{bmatrix}$, (b) $\begin{bmatrix} -24 & -30 \\ 60 & 36 \end{bmatrix}$.

14. (a) $\begin{bmatrix} 4/9 \\ 5/9 \end{bmatrix}$, (b) $\begin{bmatrix} 3/7 \\ 4/7 \end{bmatrix}$.

T.1. (b) The (i,j) entry of $A + (B+C)$ is $a_{ij} + (b_{ij} + c_{ij})$, that of $(A+B) + C$ is $(a_{ij} + b_{ij}) + c_{ij}$. These two entries are equal because of the associative law for addition of real numbers.

    (d) For each (i,j) let $d_{ij} = -a_{ij}$, $D = [d_{ij}]$. Then $A + D = D + A = 0$.

T.2. $\displaystyle\sum_{p=1}^{3} a_{ip} \left(\sum_{q=1}^{4} b_{pq}c_{qj} \right) = \sum_{p=1}^{3} \sum_{q=1}^{4} a_{ip}b_{pq}c_{qj}$

$\displaystyle = \sum_{q=1}^{4} \sum_{p=1}^{3} a_{ip}b_{pq}c_{qj} = \sum_{q=1}^{4} \left(\sum_{p=1}^{3} a_{ip}b_{pq} \right) c_{qj}.$

T.3.
(b) $\displaystyle\sum_{k=1}^{p} a_{ik}(b_{kj}+c_{kj}) = \sum_{k=1}^{p} (a_{ik}b_{kj}+a_{ik}c_{kj}) = \sum_{k=1}^{p} a_{ik}b_{kj} + \sum_{k=1}^{p} a_{ik}c_{kj}$

(c) $\displaystyle\sum_{k=1}^{p} (a_{ik}+b_{ik})c_{kj} = \sum_{k=1}^{p} (a_{ik}c_{kj}+b_{ik}c_{kj}) = \sum_{k=1}^{p} a_{ik}c_{kj} + \sum_{k=1}^{p} b_{ik}c_{kj}.$

T.4. Denote the entries of the identity matrix by d_{ij}, so that

$$d_{ij} = \begin{cases} 1 & \text{if } i=j \\ 0 & \text{if } i \neq j \end{cases}.$$

Then for $C = AI_n$, $c_{ij} = \sum_{k=1}^{p} a_{ik}d_{kj} = a_{ij}d_{jj}$ (all other d_{kj} are

zero), $= a_{ij}$, and thus $C = A$. Similar argument shows $I_m A = A$.

T.5. $A^p A^q = \underbrace{(A \cdot A \cdots A)}_{p \text{ factors}} \cdot \underbrace{(A \cdot A \cdots A)}_{q \text{ factors}} = A^{p+q}$,

$$\underbrace{}_{p+q \text{ factors}}$$

$$(A^p)^q = \underbrace{A^p \cdot A^p \cdot A^p \cdots A^p}_{q \text{ factors}} = \underbrace{A^{p+p+\cdots p}}_{q \text{ summands}} = A^{pq}.$$

T.6. We are given that $AB = BA$.

For $p=2$, $(AB)(AB) = A(BA)B = A(AB)B = AB$. Assume that for
$p=k$, $(AB) = A^k B^k$. Then $(AB)^{k+1} = (AB)^k (AB) = A^k B^k \cdot A \cdot B$
$= A^k(B^{k-1}AB)B = A^k(B^{k-2}AB^2)B = \cdots = A^{k+1}B^{k+1}$. Thus the result
is true also for $p = k+1$. Hence it is true for all positive
integers p.
$$\text{For } p = 0, \quad (AB)^0 = I_n = A^0 B^0.$$

T.7. For $p = 0$, $(cA)^0 = I_n = 1 \cdot I_n = c^0 \cdot A^0$.

For $p = 1$, $cA = cA$.

Assume the result true for $p = k$: $(cA)^k = c^k A^k$, then for $k+1$:

$(cA)^{k+1} = (cA)^k (cA) = c^k A^k \cdot cA = c^k(A^k c)A = c^k(cA^k)A$

$= (c^k c)(A^k A) = c^{k+1}A^{k+1}.$

T.8. (a) For $A = [a_{ij}]$, the (i,j) element of $r(sA)$ is $r(sa_{ij})$,
that of $(rs)A$ is $(rs)a_{ij}$, and these are equal by the
associative law for multiplication of real numbers.

(b) The (i,j) element of $(r+s)A$ is $(r+s)a_{ij}$, that of $rA + sA$
is $ra_{ij} + sa_{ij}$, and these are equal by the distributive
law.

(c) $r(a_{ij}+b_{ij}) = ra_{ij} + rb_{ij}$.

(d) $\sum_{k=1}^{p} a_{ik}(rb_{kj}) = r\sum_{k=1}^{p} a_{ik}b_{kj} = \sum_{k=1}^{p} (ra_{ik})b_{kj}.$

T.9. $(-1)a_{ij} = -a_{ij}$ (see Ex. T.1.).

T.10.(a) The i,jth element of $(A^T)^T$ is the j,ith element of A^T, which is the i,jth element of A.

   (b) The i,jth element of $(A+B)^T$ is c_{ji} where $c_{ij} = a_{ij} + b_{ij}$. Thus $c_{ji} = a_{ji} + b_{ji}$. Hence $(A+B)^T = A^T + B^T$.

   (c) The i,jth element of $(rA)^T$ is the j,ith element of rA, that is ra_{ji}. Thus $(rA)^T = rA^T$.

T.11. If A is symmetric, then $A^T = A$. Thus $a_{ji} = a_{ij}$ for all i and j. Conversely, if $a_{ji} = a_{ij}$ for all i and j, then $A^T = A$ and A is symmetric.

T.12. Both "A is symmetric" and "A^T is symmetric" are logically equivalent to "$a_{ji} = a_{ij}$ for all i and j."

T.13. (a) $(A+B)^T = A^T + B^T = A + B$, so $A + B$ is symmetric,

   (b) Suppose that AB is symmetric.
   Then $(AB)^T = AB$
   $$B^T A^T = AB \qquad \text{(Thm. 1.4(c))}$$
   $$BA = AB \qquad \text{(A and B are each symmetric)}$$
   Thus A and B commute. Conversely, if A and B commute, then $(AB)^T = AB$ and AB is symmetric.

T.14. Suppose A is skew symmetric. Then the j,ith element of A equals $-a_{ij}$. That is, $a_{ij} = -a_{ji}$.

T.15. (a) $(AA^T)^T = (A^T)^T A^T \qquad \text{(Thm.1.4(c))}$
   $$= AA^T \qquad \text{(Thm.1.4(a))}$$
   Thus AA^T is symmetric. A similar argument applies to $A^T A$.

   (b) $(A+A^T)^T = A^T + (A^T)^T = A^T + A = A + A^T$.

   (c) $(A-A^T)^T = A^T - (A^T)^T = A^T - A = -(A - A^T)$.

T.16. Let $S = 1/2(A + A^T)$ and $K = (1/2)(A - A^T)$. Then S is symmetric and K is skew symmetric, by Exercise T.15.

$$S + K = 1/2(A + A^T + A - A^T) = (1/2)(2A) = A.$$

Conversely, suppose $A = S + K$ is any decomposition of A into the sum of a symmetric and a skew symmetric matrix. Then

$$A^T = (S + K)^T = S^T + K^T = S - K$$

$$A + A^T = (S + K) + (S - K) = 2S, \quad S = (1/2)(A + A^T),$$

$$A - A^T = (S + K) - (S - K) = 2K, \quad K = (1/2)(A - A^T).$$

T.17. If the diagonal entries of A are r, then since $r = r \cdot 1$, $A = rI_n$.

T.18. $I_n = [d_{ij}]$ where $d_{ij} = \begin{cases} 1 & \text{if } i=j \\ 0 & \text{if } i \neq j \end{cases}$.

Then $d_{ji} = \begin{cases} 1 & \text{if } i=j \\ 0 & \text{if } i \neq j \end{cases}$. Thus $I_n^T = I_n$.

T.19. Suppose $r \neq 0$. The i,jth entry of rA is ra_{ij}. Since $r \neq 0$, $a_{ij} = 0$ for all i and j. Thus $A = 0$.

T.20. Let X_1 and X_2 be two (distinct) solutions to the linear system $AX = B$, and consider $X_3 = rX_1 + sX_2$ for $r + s = 1$. X_3 is a solution to the system since $AX_3 = A(rX_1 + sX_2)$ $= r(AX_1) + s(AX_2) = rB + sB = (r+s)B = B$.

If $B = 0$, then one at least of X_1, X_2 must be nonzero, say X_1, and then the infinitely many matrices rX_1, r a real number, constitute solutions.

If $B \neq 0$, then X_1 and X_2 cannot be nontrivial multiples of each other. (If $X_2 = tX_1$, $t \neq 1$, then $AX_2 = tB \neq B = AX_1$, contradiction.) Thus, if $rX_1 + sX_2 = r'X_1 + s'X_2$ for some r,s,r',s', then

$$(r - r')X_1 = (s' - s)X_2,$$

whence $r = r'$ and $s = s'$. Therefore the matrices $X_3 = rX_1 + sX_2$ are distinct as r ranges over real numbers and $s = 1 - r$.

T.21. Suppose $A = \begin{bmatrix} a & b \\ c & d \end{bmatrix}$ satisfies $AB = BA$ for any 2×2

matrix B. Choosing $B = \begin{bmatrix} 1 & 0 \\ 0 & 0 \end{bmatrix}$ we get

$$\begin{bmatrix} a & b \\ c & d \end{bmatrix} \begin{bmatrix} 1 & 0 \\ 0 & 0 \end{bmatrix} = \begin{bmatrix} 1 & 0 \\ 0 & 0 \end{bmatrix} \begin{bmatrix} a & b \\ c & d \end{bmatrix}$$

$$\begin{bmatrix} a & 0 \\ c & 0 \end{bmatrix} = \begin{bmatrix} a & b \\ 0 & 0 \end{bmatrix}$$

which implies $b = c = 0$. Thus $A = \begin{bmatrix} a & 0 \\ 0 & d \end{bmatrix}$ is diagonal.

Next choosing $B = \begin{bmatrix} 0 & 1 \\ 0 & 0 \end{bmatrix}$ we get $\begin{bmatrix} 0 & a \\ 0 & 0 \end{bmatrix} = \begin{bmatrix} 0 & d \\ 0 & 0 \end{bmatrix}$,

or $a = d$. Thus $A = \begin{bmatrix} a & 0 \\ 0 & a \end{bmatrix}$ is a scalar matrix.

Section 1.4, page 47

2.(a) $\begin{bmatrix} 1 & 0 & 3 \\ 5 & -1 & 5 \\ 4 & 2 & 2 \\ -3 & 1 & 4 \end{bmatrix}$; (b) $\begin{bmatrix} 1 & 0 & 3 \\ -3 & 1 & 4 \\ 12 & 6 & 6 \\ 5 & -1 & 5 \end{bmatrix}$; (c) $\begin{bmatrix} 1 & 0 & 3 \\ -3 & 1 & 4 \\ 4 & 2 & 2 \\ 2 & -1 & -4 \end{bmatrix}$.

4. Possible answers:

(a) $\begin{bmatrix} 2 & -1 & 3 & 4 \\ 5 & 2 & -3 & 4 \\ 0 & 1 & 2 & -1 \end{bmatrix}$; (b) $\begin{bmatrix} 4 & -2 & 6 & 8 \\ 0 & 1 & 2 & -1 \\ 5 & 2 & -3 & 4 \end{bmatrix}$;

(c) $\begin{bmatrix} 2 & -1 & 3 & 4 \\ 0 & 1 & 2 & -1 \\ 7 & 1 & 0 & 8 \end{bmatrix}$.

6. $\begin{bmatrix} 0 & 1 & 0 & 0 & 0 \\ 0 & 0 & 1 & 0 & 0 \\ 0 & 0 & 0 & 1 & 0 \\ 0 & 0 & 0 & 0 & 1 \end{bmatrix}$.

8.(a) x = 1, y = 2, z = -2;

  (b) No solution;

  (c) x = 1, y = 1, z = 0.

10. (a) x = 1, y = -1, z = 0;

   (b) x = 1 - r, y = 3 + r, z = 2 - r, w = r;

   (c) No solution.

12. (i) a = $\pm\sqrt{3}$, (ii) a ≠ $\pm\sqrt{3}$, (iii) none.

14. (i) a = -3, (ii) a ≠ ± 3, (iii) a = 3.

16. (a) x = r, y = -2r, z = r, r = any real number;

   (b) x = 1, y = 2, z = 2.

18. (a) No solution; (b) x = 1 - r, y = 2 + r, z = -1 + r, w = r,

   r = any real number.

20. x = 5r, y = 6r, z = r, r = any real number.

22. 60 in deluxe binding. If r is the number in bookclub binding, then r is an integer which must satisfy 0 ≤ r ≤ 90 and then the number of paperbacks is 180 - 2r.

T.1. Suppose the leading entry of the ith row occurs in the jth column. Since leading entries of rows i+1, i+2,... are to the right of that of the ith row, and in any nonzero row, the leading entry is the first nonzero element, all entries in the jth column below the ith row must be zero.

T.2. (a) A is row equivalent to itself: the sequence of operations is the empty sequence.

   (b) Each elementary row operation of types (a), (b) or (c) has a corresponding inverse operation of the same type which "undoes" the effect of the original operation. For example, the inverse of the operation "add d times row r of A to row s of A " is "subtract d times row r of A from from row s of A." Since B is assumed row equivalent to A, there is a sequence of elementary row operations which gets from A to B. Take those operations in the reverse order, and for each operation do its inverse, and that takes B to A. Thus A is row equivalent to B.

   (c) Follow the operations which take A to B with those which take B to C.

T.3. The sequence of elementary row operations which takes **A** to **B**,
when applied to the augmented matrix [A┆0], yields the augmented matrix [B┆0]. Thus both systems have the same solutions,
by Theorem 1.6.

T.4. A linear system whose augmented matrix has the row
$$[0 \ 0 \ 0 \cdots 0 | 1] \qquad\qquad (*)$$
can have no solution: that row corresponds to the unsolvable
equation $0X_1 + 0X_2 + \cdots + 0X_n = 1$. If the augmented matrix of
AX = **B** is row equivalent to a matrix with the row (*) above,
then by Theorem 1.6, **AX** = **B** can have no solution.

Conversely, assume **AX** = **B** has no solution. Its augmented
matrix is row equivalent to some matrix [C┆D] in reduced row
echelon form. If [C┆D] does not contain the row (*) then it
has at most m nonzero rows, and the leading entries of those
nonzero rows all correspond to unknowns of the system. After
assigning values to the free variables -- the variables not
corresponding to leading entries of rows -- one gets a solution
to the system by solving for the values of the leading entry
variables. This contradicts the assumption that the system had
no solution.

T.5. If ad-bc = 0, the two rows of $A = \begin{bmatrix} a & b \\ c & d \end{bmatrix}$ are multiples of
one another: c[a b] = [ac bc] and a[c d] = [ac ad] and
bc = ad. Any elementary row operation applied to **A** will
produce a matrix with rows that are multiples of each other.
In particular, elementary row operations cannot produce I_2, and
so I_2 is not row equivalent to **A**.

If ad - bc ≠ 0, then a and c are not both 0. Suppose
a ≠ 0.

$$\left[\begin{array}{cc|cc} a & b & 1 & 0 \\ c & d & 0 & 1 \end{array}\right]$$

Multiplying the first row by $\frac{1}{a}$, and and adding $-c$ times the first row to the second row we obtain

$$\left[\begin{array}{cc|cc} 1 & \frac{b}{a} & \frac{1}{a} & 0 \\ 0 & \frac{d-bc}{a} & -c & 1 \end{array}\right]$$

Multiplying the second row by $\frac{a}{ad-bc}$ we obtain

$$\left[\begin{array}{cc|cc} 1 & \frac{b}{a} & \frac{1}{a} & 0 \\ 0 & 1 & \frac{-ac}{ad-bc} & \frac{1}{ad-bc} \end{array}\right]$$

Adding $-\frac{b}{a}$ times the second row to the first row we obtain

$$\left[\begin{array}{cc|cc} 1 & 0 & \frac{d}{ad-bc} & \frac{-b}{ad-bc} \\ 0 & 1 & \frac{-c}{ad-bc} & \frac{a}{ad-bc} \end{array}\right]$$

Hence, A is row equivalent to I_2.

T.6. By Corollary 1.1, A is row equivalent to a matrix B in reduced row echelon form which determines the same solutions as A. The possibilities for the 2×2 matrix B are I_2 and

$$\left\{ \begin{bmatrix} 1 & 0 \\ 0 & 0 \end{bmatrix}, \begin{bmatrix} 0 & 1 \\ 0 & 0 \end{bmatrix}, \begin{bmatrix} 0 & 0 \\ 0 & 0 \end{bmatrix} \right\}. \tag{*}$$

The homogeneous system $I_2 X = 0$ has only the trivial solution. The other three forms (*) clearly have nontrivial solutions. Thus $AX = B$ has only the trivial solution if and only if $ad-bc \neq 0$.

T.8. By Exercise T.6.

T.9. (a) $A(X_1 + Y_1) = AX_1 + AY_1 = B + 0 = B$,

(b) Let X_1 be a solution to $AX = B$ and let $Y_1 = X-X_1$. Then

$X = X_1 + (X-X_1) = X_1 + Y_1$ and $AY_1 = A(X-X_1) = AX - AX_1$

$= B-B = 0$.

2. Adding twice the first row to the second row produces a row of zeros.

4. Singular.

6. (a) singular; (b) $\begin{bmatrix} 1 & -1 & 0 \\ 3/2 & 1/2 & -3/2 \\ -1 & 0 & 1 \end{bmatrix}$;

(c) $\begin{bmatrix} 1 & -1 & 0 & -1 \\ 0 & -1/2 & 0 & 0 \\ -1/5 & 1 & 1/5 & 3/5 \\ 2/5 & -1/2 & -2/5 & -1/5 \end{bmatrix}$.

8. (a) $\begin{bmatrix} 1 & 0 & -1 \\ 1 & -1 & 2 \\ -1 & 1 & -1 \end{bmatrix}$; (b) $\begin{bmatrix} 3 & 2 & -4 \\ -1 & 0 & 1 \\ 0 & -1 & 1 \end{bmatrix}$; (c) singular.

10. (a) $\begin{bmatrix} 3/5 & -3/5 & -2/5 \\ 2/5 & 3/5 & -4/5 \\ -1/5 & 2/5 & 2/5 \end{bmatrix}$; (b) singular; (c) singular.

12. (b) and (c).

14. $\begin{bmatrix} -1 & -4 \\ 1 & 3 \end{bmatrix}$.

15. If the jth column A_j of A consists entirely of zeros, then so does the jth column BA_j of BA (Ex. T.5, Sect. 1.2), so A is singular.

   If the ith row A_i of A consists entirely of zeros, then for any B, the ith row A_iB of AB is zero, so again A is singular.

16. $a \neq 0$, $A^{-1} = \begin{bmatrix} 0 & 1 & 0 \\ 1 & -1 & 0 \\ -2/a & 1/a & 1/a \end{bmatrix}$.

18. (a) $A^{-1} = \begin{bmatrix} 7 & -3 \\ -2 & 1 \end{bmatrix}$; (b) $(A^T)^{-1} = \begin{bmatrix} 7 & -2 \\ -3 & 1 \end{bmatrix} = (A^{-1})^T$.

19. Yes. $(A^{-1})^T A = (A^{-1})^T A^T = (AA^{-1})^T = I_n^T = I_n$. By Theorem 1.10, $(A^{-1})^T = A^{-1}$. That is, A^{-1} is symmetric.

20. (a) No. Let $A = \begin{bmatrix} 1 & 0 \\ 0 & 0 \end{bmatrix}$, $B = \begin{bmatrix} 0 & 0 \\ 0 & 1 \end{bmatrix}$. Then $(A+B)^{-1}$ exists

but A^{-1} and B^{-1} do not. Even supposing they all exist, equality need not hold. Let $A = [1]$, $B = [2]$ so $(A+B)^{-1}$

$= [1/3] \neq [1] + [1/2] = A^{-1} + B^{-1}$.

(b) Yes for A nonsingular and $c \neq 0$.

$(cA)(\frac{1}{c}A^{-1}) = c(\frac{1}{c})A \cdot A^{-1} = 1 \cdot I_n = I_n$.

22. $A+B$ may be singular: let $A = I_n$ and $B = -I_n$.

$A-B$ may be singular: let $A = B = I_n$.

$-A$ is nonsingular: $(-A)^{-1} = -(A^{-1})$.

24. $\begin{bmatrix} 11 & 19 \\ 7 & 0 \end{bmatrix}$

T.1. B is nonsingular, so B^{-1} exists, and

$$A = AI_n = A(BB^{-1}) = (AB)B^{-1} = 0B^{-1} = 0.$$

T.2. The case $r = 2$ of Corollary 1.2 is Theorem 1.9(b). In

general, if $r > 2$, $(A_1 A_2 \cdots A_r)^{-1} = [(A_1 A_2 \cdots A_{r-1})A_r]^{-1}$

$= A_r^{-1}(A_1 A_2 \cdots A_{r-1})^{-1} = A_r^{-1}[(A_1 A_2 \cdots A_{r-2})A_{r-1}]^{-1}$

$= A_r^{-1} A_{r-1}^{-1}(A_1 A_2 \cdots A_{r-2})^{-1} = \cdots = A_r^{-1} A_{r-1}^{-1} \cdots A_1^{-1}$.

T.3. A is row equivalent to a matrix B in reduced row echelon form which, by Theorem 1.11 is not I_n. Thus B has fewer than n nonzero rows, and fewer than n variables corresponding to pivotal columns of B. Choose one of the free variables -- variables not corresponding to pivotal columns of B. Assign any nonzero value to that variable. This leads to a nontrivial solution to the homogeneous system $AX = 0$.

T.4. The result follows from Theorem 1.11 and Exercise T.5. of Section 1.4.

T.5. The zero matrix.

T.6. All diagonal matrices.

T.7. Let X_1 be one solution to AX = B. Since A is singular,
the homogeneous system AX=0 has a nontrivial solution Y_0.
Then for any real number r, $Y_1 = rY_0$ is also a solution to
the homogeneous system. Finally, by Exercise T.9.(a),
Sect. 1.4, for each of the infinitely many matrices Y_1, the
matrix $X = X_1 + Y_1$ is a solution to the nonhomogeneous
system AX = B.

Review Exercises, page 64

2. $\begin{bmatrix} 8 & -6 \\ -9 & 17 \end{bmatrix}$.

4. (a) When AB = BA, since $(A+B)(A-B) = A^2 - AB + BA - B^2$

   (b) $(AB)C = A(BC) = A(CB)$

   $= (AC)B = (CA)B$

   $= C(AB).$

6. $\begin{bmatrix} 1 & 0 & 11/5 & 0 \\ 0 & 1 & -7/5 & 0 \\ 0 & 0 & 0 & 1 \\ 0 & 0 & 0 & 0 \end{bmatrix}$

8. $x = \frac{7}{3} + \frac{2}{3}r - s$, $y = \frac{2}{3} + \frac{1}{3}r$, $z = r$, $w = s$, r and s any real
numbers.

10. $2b_1 + b_2 - b_3 = 0.$

12.   a = 1,2.

14.
$$\begin{bmatrix} 1/4 & 1/2 & -1/4 \\ 3/4 & 0 & -1/4 \\ -1/4 & 1/2 & 1/4 \end{bmatrix} .$$

16.
$$\begin{bmatrix} 3 & 5 & 0 \\ 1 & 3 & -3 \\ 7 & 10 & 4 \end{bmatrix} .$$

18.   0,4 .

20. $\frac{1}{c} A^{-1}$.

CHAPTER 2

Section 2.1, page 76

2. (a) even; (b) odd; (c) even; (d) odd; (e) even; (f) even.

4. The numbers of inversions are: (a) 9,6;   (b) 8,7;   (c) 5,6;
   (d) 2,7.

6. (a) 2;   (b) 24;   (c) -30;   (d) 2.

8. $|B| = 4$; $|C| = -8$; $|D| = -4$.

10. $|A| = |A^T| = 14$.

12. (a) $(\lambda-1)(\lambda-2)(\lambda-3) = \lambda^3 - 6\lambda^2 + 11\lambda-6$.

   (b) $\lambda^3-\lambda$.

14. (a) 1,2,3;   (b) -1,0,1.

16. (a) -120;   (b) 29;   (c) 9.

18. (a) -1;   (b) -120;   (c) -22.

20. (a) 16;   (b) 256;   (c) $-\frac{1}{4}$.

T.1. If j_i and j_{i+1} are interchanged, all inversions between
numbers distinct from j_i and j_{i+1} remain unchanged, and all
inversions between one of j_i , j_{i+1} and some other number also
remain unchanged. If originally $j_i < j_{i+1}$, then after interchange there is one additional inversion due to $j_{i+1}j_i$. If
originally $j_i > j_{i+1}$, then after interchange there is one
fewer inversion.

   Suppose j_p and j_q are separated by k invervening
numbers. Then k interchanges of adjacent numbers will move
 j_p next to j_q . One interchange switches j_p and j_q .
Finally, k interchanges of adjacent numbers takes j_q back
to j_p 's original position. The total number of interchanges
is the odd number $2k+1$.

T.2. Parallel to proof for the upper triangular case.

T.3. $cA = [ca_{ij}]$. By n applications of Theorem 2.5, the result
follows.

T.4. If A is nonsingular, then $AA^{-1} = I_n$.
   $|A| \cdot |A^{-1}| = |AA^{-1}| = |I_n| = 1$.
Thus $|A| \neq 0$ and $|A^{-1}| = 1/|A|$.

T.5. $|AB| = |A||B|$. Thus if $|AB| = 0$, $|A| \cdot |B| = 0$ and either
 $|A| = 0$ or $|B| = 0$.

T.6. $|AB| = |A| \cdot |B| = |B| \cdot |A| = |BA|$.

T.7. In the summation

$$|A| = \sum (\pm) \; a_{1j1}a_{2j2}\cdots a_{njn}$$

((2) of page 68) there is exactly one nonzero term. Thus,
 $|A| \neq 0$.

T.8. $|A||B| = |AB| = |I_n| = 1$. Thus $|A| \neq 0$ and $|B| \neq 0$.

T.9. (a) $|A|^2 = |A| \cdot |A| = |A| \cdot |A^{-1}| = |AA^{-1}| = 1$.
   (b) $|A|^2 = |A||A| = |A| \; |A^T| = |A| \; |A^{-1}| = |AA^{-1}| = 1$.

T.10. $|A^2| = |A|^2 = |A|$ so $|A|$ is a nonzero root of the equation
 $x^2 - x = 0$.

T.11. $|A^T B^T| = |A^T||B^T| = |A||B^T| = |A^T||B|$.

T.12.
$$\begin{vmatrix} 1 & a & a^2 \\ 1 & b & b^2 \\ 1 & c & c^2 \end{vmatrix} = \begin{vmatrix} 1 & a & a^2 \\ 0 & b-a & b^2-a^2 \\ 0 & c-a & c^2-a^2 \end{vmatrix} = \begin{vmatrix} b-a & (b-a)(b+a) \\ c-a & (c-a)(c+a) \end{vmatrix}$$

$$= (b-a)(c-a) \begin{vmatrix} 1 & b+a \\ 1 & c+a \end{vmatrix} = (b-a)(c-a) \begin{vmatrix} 1 & b \\ 1 & c \end{vmatrix} = (b-a)(c-a)(c-b).$$

T.13. If A is nonsingular, by Corollary 2.1, $|A| \neq 0$ and $a_{ii} \neq 0$ for $i = 1, 2, \cdots, n$. Conversely, if $a_{ii} \neq 0$ for $i = 1, \cdots, n$, then clearly A is row equivalent to I_n, and thus is nonsingular.

T.14. $|AB| = |A||B| = 0 \cdot |B| = 0$.

T.15. If $|A| \neq 0$, then since $0 = |0| = |A^n| = |A| \cdot |A^{n-1}|$, by Exercise T.5 above, $|A^{n-1}| = 0$. Working downward, $|A^{n-2}| = 0, \ldots, |A^2| = 0, |A| = 0$, which is a contradiction.

T.16. $|A| = |A^T| = |-A| = (-1)^n |A| = -|A|$, which implies $|A| = 0$.

Section 2.2, page 89

2. $A_{21} = 0$, $A_{22} = 0$, $A_{23} = 0$, $A_{24} = 13$, $A_{13} = -9$, $A_{23} = 0$, $A_{33} = 3$, $A_{43} = -2$.

4. (a) 9; (b) 13; (c) -26.

6. (a) -135; (b) -20; (c) -20.

8. (a) $\begin{bmatrix} 2 & -7 & -6 \\ 1 & -7 & -3 \\ -4 & 7 & 5 \end{bmatrix}$; (b) -7.

10. (a) $\begin{bmatrix} 2/9 & -1/9 \\ 1/6 & 1/6 \end{bmatrix}$; (b) $\begin{bmatrix} 3/14 & -3/7 & 1/7 \\ 1/7 & 5/7 & -4/7 \\ -1/14 & 1/7 & 2/7 \end{bmatrix}$; (c) Singular.

12. (a) $\begin{bmatrix} 1 & 0 & -1 \\ -2 & 1/2 & 5/2 \\ -1 & 0 & 2 \end{bmatrix}$; (b) $\begin{bmatrix} 1/3 & -1/3 \\ & \\ -2/3 & -5/3 \end{bmatrix}$;

(c) $\begin{bmatrix} -1/21 & -2/21 & 8/21 \\ 4/21 & -5/42 & -1/42 \\ 7/42 & 7/84 & -7/84 \end{bmatrix}$.

14. (a), (b) and (d) are nonsingular.

16. (a) $0,5$;   (b) $-1,0,1$.

18. (a) has nontrivial solutions; (b) has only the trivial solution.

20. $x = -2$, $y = 0$, $z = 1$.

22. $x = 22/5$, $y = -26/5$, $z = 12/5$.

T.1. Let **A** be upper triangular. Then

$$|A| = \begin{vmatrix} a_{11} & a_{12} & \cdots & a_{1n} \\ 0 & a_{22} & \cdots & a_{2n} \\ \vdots & \vdots & & \vdots \\ 0 & 0 & \cdots & a_{nn} \end{vmatrix} = a_{11}A_{11} = a_{11} \begin{vmatrix} a_{22} & \cdots & a_{2n} \\ 0 & \cdots & \\ 0 & \cdots & a_{nn} \end{vmatrix}$$

$$= a_{11}a_{22} \begin{vmatrix} a_{33} & \cdots & a_{3n} \\ & \ddots & \\ 0 & & a_{nn} \end{vmatrix} = \cdots = a_{11}a_{22}\cdots a_{nn}.$$

T.2. (a) $|A| = -a_{12} \begin{vmatrix} a_{21} & a_{23} \\ a_{31} & a_{33} \end{vmatrix} + a_{22} \begin{vmatrix} a_{11} & a_{13} \\ a_{31} & a_{33} \end{vmatrix} - a_{32} \begin{vmatrix} a_{11} & a_{13} \\ a_{21} & a_{23} \end{vmatrix}$

$= -a_{12}(a_{21}a_{33} - a_{23}a_{31}) + a_{22}(a_{11}a_{33} - a_{13}a_{31})$

$\quad - a_{32}(a_{11}a_{23} - a_{13}a_{21})$

$= -a_{12}a_{21}a_{33} + a_{12}a_{23}a_{31} + a_{11}a_{22}a_{33} - a_{13}a_{22}a_{31} - a_{11}a_{23}a_{32}$

$\quad + a_{13}a_{21}a_{32}.$

T.3. The i,j entry of adj A is $A_{ji} = (-1)^{j+i}|M_{ji}|$ where M_{ji} is the submatrix of A obtained by deleting from A the jth row and ith column. Since A is symmetric, that submatrix is the transpose of M_{ij}. Thus $A_{ji} = (-1)^{j+i}|M_{ji}| = (-1)^{i+j}|M_{ij}| =$ j,i entry of adj A . Thus adj A is symmetric.

T.4. The adjoint matrix is upper triangular if A is upper triangular, since $A_{ij} = 0$ if $i > j$.

T.5. If $|A| = ad-bc \neq 0$, then by Corollary 2.2, $A^{-1} = \dfrac{1}{|A|}$ (adj A)

$$= \frac{1}{ad-bc} \begin{vmatrix} d & -b \\ -c & a \end{vmatrix}.$$

T.6. $\dfrac{1}{(b-a)(c-a)(c-b)} \begin{bmatrix} bc(c-b) & ac(a-c) & ab(b-a) \\ b^2 - c^2 & c^2 - a^2 & a^2 - b^2 \\ c - b & a - c & b - a \end{bmatrix}$.

T.7. If A = 0 then adj A = 0 and is singular. Suppose $A \neq 0$ but is singular. By Theorem 2.11, A(adj A) = $|A|I_n = 0$. Were adj A nonsingular, it would have an inverse, and

$A = A(\text{adj } A)(\text{adj } A)^{-1} = 0(\text{adj } A)^{-1} = 0.$

Contradiction.

T.8. For the case that A is nonsingular, we have adj A = $|A|A^{-1}$. Hence $|\text{adj } A| = \left||A|A^{-1}\right| = |A|^n|A^{-1}| = |A|^n \dfrac{1}{|A|} = |A|^{n-1}$.

T.9. $\begin{vmatrix} a - \lambda & b \\ c & d - \lambda \end{vmatrix} = (a-\lambda)(d-\lambda) - bc.$

T.10. If $|A| \neq 0$ then A is nonsingular, and $B = A^{-1}AB = A^{-1}AC = C$.

T.11.   Since the entries of A are integers, the cofactors of entries
        of A are integers and adj A is a matrix of integer entries.
        Since $|A| = \pm 1$, A^{-1} is also a matrix of integers.

T.12. $\left(\dfrac{1}{|A|} A\right)$ adj A $= \dfrac{|A|}{|A|} I_n = I_n$. Thus $\dfrac{1}{|A|} A = (\text{adj } A)^{-1}$.

   By Corollary 2.2, for any nonsingular B,

   $$\text{adj } B = |B| B^{-1}. \text{ Thus for } B = A^{-1}$$

   $$\text{adj}(A^{-1}) = |A^{-1}| (A^{-1})^{-1} = \dfrac{1}{|A|} A.$$

Review Exercises, page 94

2. (a) 5/2 ;   (b) 30 .

4. (a) 12 ;   (b) 36 ;   (c) 3 .

6. -2 .

8. $A_{11} = 44$, $A_{12} = -21$, $A_{13} = 8$

    $A_{21} = -6$, $A_{22} = 21$, $A_{23} = 11$

    $A_{31} = -17$, $A_{32} = -7$, $A_{33} = 9$.

10. (a) $\begin{bmatrix} -7 & 8 & -13 \\ 5 & 4 & -15 \\ -4 & -10 & 12 \end{bmatrix}$;   (b) -34 .

12. -2,0 .

14. x = -2, y = 1, z = -3.

Chapter 3

Section 3.1, page 109

2.

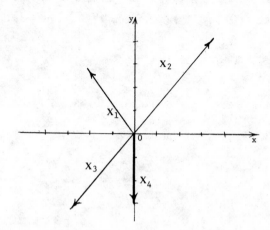

4. (-1,-3)

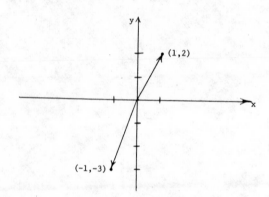

6. (a) X + Y = (1,7); X - Y = (-3,-1); 2X = (-2,6);
      3X - 2Y = (-7, 1);

   (b) X + Y = (1,-1); X - Y = (-9,-5); 2X = (-8,-6);
      3X - 2Y = (-22, -13);

   (c) X + Y = (1,2); X - Y = (5,2); 2X = (6,4); 3X - 2Y = (13,6).

8. (a) x = -2, y = -9;   (b) x = -6, y = 8;   (c) x = 5, y = -25/2.

10. (a) $\sqrt{13}$;   (b) 3;   (c) $\sqrt{41}$;   (d) $\sqrt{13}$.

12. (a) 3; (b) $\sqrt{20}$; (c) $\sqrt{18}$ (d) $\sqrt{5}$.

14. (a) $\left(\dfrac{1}{\sqrt{5}}, \dfrac{2}{\sqrt{5}}\right)$; (b) $(0, -1)$; (c) $\left(-\dfrac{1}{\sqrt{10}}, -\dfrac{3}{\sqrt{10}}\right)$.

16. (a) 0; (b) -2; (c) -4 ; (d) -6 .

18. (a) 0 ; (b) $\dfrac{-1}{\sqrt{2}\,\sqrt{41}}$; (c) $\dfrac{-4}{\sqrt{5}\,\sqrt{13}}$; (d) $-\dfrac{1}{\sqrt{2}}$.

20. (a) X_1 and X_4, X_1 and X_6, X_3 and X_4, X_3 and X_6, X_4 and X_5, X_5 and X_6 ;

    (b) X_1 and X_5, X_4 and X_6 ;

    (c) X_1 and X_3 , X_3 and X_5.

22. (a) $\begin{bmatrix} 3 \\ -2 \end{bmatrix}$; (b) $\begin{bmatrix} 2 \\ 0 \end{bmatrix}$; (c) $\begin{bmatrix} -2 \\ -3 \end{bmatrix}$.

24.

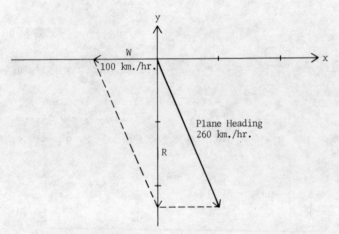

Resultant speed: 240 km./hr.

T.1. Locate the point A on the x-axis which is x units from the origin. Construct a perpendicular to the x-axis through A. Locate B on the y-axis y units from the origin. Construct a perpendicular through B. The intersection of those two perpendiculars is the desired point in the plane.

T.2. $(x,y) + (0,0) = (x+0,\ y+0) = (x,y)$.

T.3. $(x,y) + (-1)(x,y) = (x,y) + (-x,-y) = (x-x, y-y) = (0,0)$.

T.4. $\|cX\| = \sqrt{(cx)^2 + (cy)^2} = \sqrt{c^2}\sqrt{x^2+y^2} = |c| \ \|X\|$

T.5. $\|U\| = \left\|\dfrac{1}{\|X\|} \ X\right\| = \dfrac{1}{\|X\|} \cdot \|X\| = 1.$

T.6. (a) $1 \cdot (x,y) = (1 \cdot x, \ 1 \cdot y) = (x,y),$

     (b) $(rs)(x,y) = (rsx, \ rsy) = r(sx, \ sy) = r(sX).$

T.7. (a) $X \cdot X = \|X\|^2 = x^2 + y^2; \ x^2 + y^2 \ge 0 ; \ = 0$ if and only
       if $x = 0$ and $y = 0,$

     (b) $(x_1,y_1) \cdot (x_2,y_2) = x_1 x_2 + y_1 y_2 = x_2 x_1 + y_2 y_1 = (x_2,y_2) \cdot (x_1,y_1),$

     (c) $[(x_1,y_1)+(x_2,y_2)] \cdot (x_3,y_3) = (x_1+x_2)x_3 + (y_1+y_2)y_3$

          $= x_1 x_3 + y_1 y_3 + x_2 x_3 + y_2 y_3 = (x_1,y_1) \cdot (x_3,y_3)+(x_2,y_2) \cdot (x_3,y_3),$

     (d) $(cx_1,cy_1) \cdot (x_2,y_2) = cx_1 x_2 + cy_1 y_2 = (x_1,y_1) \cdot (cx_2,cy_2)$

          $= c(x_1 x_2+y_1 y_2) = c[(x_1,y_1) \cdot (x_2,y_2)].$

T.8. If $Z \cdot X = 0 = Z \cdot Y,$ then $Z \cdot (rX + sY) = r(Z \cdot X) + s(Z \cdot Y) = 0+0 = 0.$

Section 3.2, page 123

2. (a) $X + Y = (5, 2, -3),$ $X - Y = (-1, -2, -5),$ $2X = (4, 0, -8),$
    $3X - 2Y = (0, -4, -14).$
  (b) $X + Y = (-1, 6, 2, -2),$ $X - Y = (-5, 4, -8, 2),$
    $2X = (-6, 10, -6, 0),$ $3X - 2Y = (-13, 13, -19, 4).$

4. (a) $x = 4/3, \ y = 1;$ (b) $x = 2, \ y = -1, \ u = 2, \ v = 4;$
  (c) $x = 7, \ y = 4.$

8. (a) $\begin{bmatrix} -2 \\ -3 \\ 3 \end{bmatrix}$; (b) $\begin{bmatrix} -1 \\ 0 \\ 1 \end{bmatrix}$; (c) $\begin{bmatrix} 4 \\ 6 \\ 8 \end{bmatrix}$; (d) $\begin{bmatrix} -1 \\ -1 \\ -2 \end{bmatrix}$.

10. (a) $\sqrt{14}$; (b) $\sqrt{30}$; (c) $\sqrt{10}$; (d) 5.

12. (a) $\sqrt{5}$; (b) $\sqrt{6}$; (c) $\sqrt{13}$; (d) $\sqrt{30}$.

14. (a) 19 ; (b) -4 ; (c) 0 ; (d) -11 .

16. (a) $X \cdot X = 1^2 + 2^2 + 3^2 = 1 + 4 + 9 = 14 \ge 0,$
   (b) $X \cdot Y = -7 = Y \cdot X,$
   (c) $(X+Y) \cdot Z = (2,4,-1) \cdot (1,0,2) = 0;$
     $X \cdot Z+Y \cdot Z = (1,2,3) \cdot (1,0,2)+(1,2,-4) \cdot (1,0,2) = 7 - 7 = 0,$
   (d) $(3,6,9) \cdot (1,2,-4) = (1,2,3) \cdot (3,6,-12) = -21 = 3(-7).$

18. (a) $\dfrac{19}{\sqrt{14}\ \sqrt{57}}$; (b) $-\dfrac{2}{7}$; (c) 0 ; (d) $\dfrac{-11}{\sqrt{14}\ \sqrt{39}}$.

22. $\| X+Y \| = \|(2,2,1,2)\| = \sqrt{4+4+1+4} = \sqrt{13} \le \sqrt{15} + \sqrt{14}$

$= \|(1,2,3,-1)\| + \|(1,0,-2,3)\|$.

24. (a) $(1/\sqrt{6},\ 2/\sqrt{6},\ -1/\sqrt{6})$; (b) $(0,\ 0,\ 1,\ 0)$;

(c) $\left(\dfrac{-1}{\sqrt{5}},\ 0,\ \dfrac{-2}{\sqrt{5}} \right)$; (d) $\left(0,\ 0,\ \dfrac{3}{5},\ \dfrac{4}{5} \right)$.

26. $\begin{bmatrix} 2 \\ 3 \\ -4 \end{bmatrix}$; (b) $\begin{bmatrix} 1 \\ 2 \\ 0 \end{bmatrix}$; (c) $\begin{bmatrix} -3 \\ 0 \\ 0 \end{bmatrix}$; (d) $\begin{bmatrix} 3 \\ 0 \\ -2 \end{bmatrix}$.

30. The value of the inventory of the four types of items.

T.1.

(a) $X + Y = \begin{bmatrix} x_1 + y_1 \\ \vdots \\ x_n + y_n \end{bmatrix} = \begin{bmatrix} y_1 + x_1 \\ \vdots \\ y_n + x_n \end{bmatrix} = Y + X$,

(b) $X + (Y+Z) = \begin{bmatrix} x_1 + (y_1+z_1) \\ \vdots \\ x_n + (y_n+z_n) \end{bmatrix} = \begin{bmatrix} (x_1+y_1) + z_1 \\ \vdots \\ (x_n+y_n) + z_n \end{bmatrix} = (X+Y) + Z$,

(c) $X + 0 = \begin{bmatrix} x_1 + 0 \\ \vdots \\ x_n + 0 \end{bmatrix} = \begin{bmatrix} x_1 \\ \vdots \\ x_n \end{bmatrix} = X$,

(d) $X + (-X) = \begin{bmatrix} x_1 + (-x_1) \\ \vdots \\ x_n + (-x_n) \end{bmatrix} = \begin{bmatrix} 0 \\ \vdots \\ 0 \end{bmatrix} = 0$,

(e) $c(X+Y) = \begin{bmatrix} c(x_1+y_1) \\ \vdots \\ c(x_n+y_n) \end{bmatrix} = \begin{bmatrix} cx_1 + cy_1 \\ \vdots \\ cx_n + cy_n \end{bmatrix} = cX + cY$,

(g) $c(dX) = \begin{bmatrix} c(dx_1) \\ \cdot \\ \cdot \\ \cdot \\ c(dx_n) \end{bmatrix} = \begin{bmatrix} (cd)x_1 \\ \cdot \\ \cdot \\ \cdot \\ (cd)x_n \end{bmatrix} = (cd)X$,

(h) $1X = \begin{bmatrix} 1x_1 \\ \cdot \\ \cdot \\ \cdot \\ 1x_n \end{bmatrix} = X.$

T.2. $X + (-1)X = (1 + (-1))X = 0 \cdot X = 0.$

Thus, $(-1)X = -X.$

T.3. The origin O and the head of the vector X, call it P, are opposite vertices of a parallelepiped with faces parallel to the coordinate planes (See Figure.)

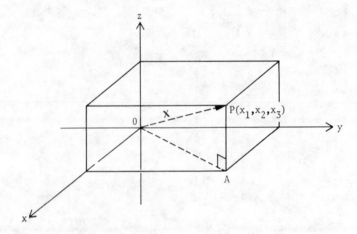

The face diagonal OA has length $\sqrt{x_1^2 + x_2^2}$ by one application of the Pythagorean Theorem. By a second application, the body diagonal has length

$$\|X\| = OP = \sqrt{\left(\sqrt{x_1^2 + x_1^2}\right)^2 + x_3^2}$$

$$= \sqrt{x_1^2 + x_2^2 + x_3^2} \ .$$

T.4. (a) $x_1^2 + x_2^2 + \cdots + x_n^2 \geq 0$ and $= 0$ if and only if all $x_i = 0$,

    (b) $\sum\limits_{i=1}^{n} x_i y_i = \sum\limits_{i=1}^{n} y_i x_i$,

    (c) $\sum\limits_{i=1}^{n} (x_i + y_i) z_i = \sum\limits_{i=1}^{n} x_i z_i + \sum\limits_{i=1}^{n} y_i z_i$,

    (d) $\sum\limits_{i=1}^{n} (cx_i) y_i = \sum\limits_{i=1}^{n} x_i (cy_i) = c \sum\limits_{i=1}^{n} x_i y_i$.

T.5. See solution to Exercise T.8. of Section 3.1.

T.6. If $X \cdot Y = 0$ for all Y, then in particular, for $Y = X$,
$0 = X \cdot X = \|X\|^2$. By (a) of Theorem 3.3, $X = 0$.

T.7. $\sum\limits_{i=1}^{n} x_i (y_i + z_i) = \sum\limits_{i=1}^{n} x_i y_i + \sum\limits_{i=1}^{n} x_i z_i$.

T.8. If $X \cdot Y = X \cdot Z$ for all X, then $X \cdot (Y-Z) = 0$ for all X.
The result follows by Exercise T.6.

T.9. $\|cX\| = \left[\sum\limits_{i=1}^{n} (cx_i)^2 \right]^{1/2} = \left[c^2 \sum\limits_{i=1}^{n} x_i^2 \right]^{1/2} = |c| \; \|X\|$.

T.10. $\|X+Y\|^2 = (X+Y) \cdot (X+Y)$

    $= X \cdot (X+Y) + Y \cdot (X+Y) = X \cdot X + X \cdot Y + Y \cdot X + Y \cdot Y$

    $= \|X\|^2 + \|Y\|^2 + 2(X \cdot Y)$

Thus $\|X+Y\|^2 = \|X\|^2 + \|Y\|^2$ if and only if $X \cdot Y = 0$.

T.11. $\sum\limits_{i=1}^{n} x_i y_i = [x_1 \; x_2 \; \cdots x_n] \begin{bmatrix} y_1 \\ y_2 \\ \cdot \\ \cdot \\ \cdot \\ y_n \end{bmatrix}$.

T.12. (a) and (b) follow from Theorem 3.3(a).
    For (c): $\|X-Y\| = \|-(Y-X)\| = \|Y-X\|$.
    (d) follows from the Triangle Inequality, Theorem 3.5.

T.13. As in the solution to Exercise T.10 above,

$$\|X+Y\|^2 = \|X\|^2 + \|Y\|^2 + 2(X\cdot Y).$$

Substitute $-Y$ for Y: $\|X-Y\|^2 = \|X\|^2 + \|Y\|^2 - 2(X\cdot Y)$

Add these two equations:

$$\|X+Y\|^2 + \|X-Y\|^2 = 2\|X\|^2 + 2\|Y\|^2.$$

T.14. $U = cX$ for $c = 1/\|X\| > 0$. Thus U is a vector in the direction of X. $\|U\| = |c| \ \|X\| = \dfrac{\|X\|}{\|X\|} = 1$.

Section 3.3, page 130

2. (a) $-4i + 4j + 4k$
   (b) $3i - 8j - k$
   (c) $0i + 0j + 0k$
   (d) $4i + 4j + 8k$

10. $\frac{1}{2} \sqrt{90}$.

12. 1 .

T.1. (a) Interchange of the second and third rows of the determinant in (2) changes the sign of that determinant.

(b)
$$\begin{vmatrix} i & j & k \\ x_1 & x_2 & x_3 \\ y_1+z_1 & y_2+z_2 & y_3+z_3 \end{vmatrix} = \begin{vmatrix} i & j & k \\ x_1 & x_2 & x_3 \\ y_1 & y_2 & y_3 \end{vmatrix} + \begin{vmatrix} i & j & k \\ x_1 & x_2 & x_3 \\ z_1 & z_2 & z_3 \end{vmatrix}.$$

(c) Similar to proof for (b).

(d) Follows from the homogeneity property for determinants: Theorem 2.5.

(e) Follows from Theorem 2.3.

(f) Follows from Theorem 2.4.

(g) First let $Z = i$. $(X\times Y)\times i = (x_1 y_2 - x_2 y_1)j$

$- (x_3 y_1 - x_1 y_3)k = x_1(y_1 i + y_2 j + y_3 k) - y_1(x_1 i + x_2 j + x_3 k)$

$= x_1 Y - y_1 X = (i\cdot X)Y - (i\cdot Y)X.$

Thus equality holds when $Z = i$. Similarly it holds when $Z = j$, when $Z = k$, and (adding scalar multiples of the 3 equations), when $Z = z_1 i + z_2 j + z_3 k$.

T.2. $(X \times Y) \cdot Z = \begin{vmatrix} z_1 & z_2 & z_3 \\ x_1 & x_2 & x_3 \\ y_1 & y_2 & y_3 \end{vmatrix} = \begin{vmatrix} x_1 & x_2 & x_3 \\ y_1 & y_2 & y_3 \\ z_1 & z_2 & z_3 \end{vmatrix} = X \cdot (Y \times Z).$

T.3. By Theorem 3.6 (a), (d), and (g),

$X \times (Y \times Z) = -(Y \times Z) \times X = -[(X \cdot Y)Z - (X \cdot Z)Y] = (X \cdot Z)Y - (X \cdot Y)Z.$

T.4. $(X \times Y) \cdot Z = (x_2 y_3 - x_3 y_2)z_1 + (x_3 y_1 - x_1 y_3)z_2 + (x_1 y_2 - x_2 y_1)z_3$

$= \begin{vmatrix} x_1 & x_2 & x_3 \\ y_1 & y_2 & y_3 \\ z_1 & z_2 & z_3 \end{vmatrix}$ (expand the determinant about the third row).

T.5. If $Y = cX$ for some c, then $X \times Y = c(X \times X) = 0$. Conversely, if $X \times Y = 0$, the area of the parallelogram with adjacent sides X and Y is 0, and hence that parallelogram is degenerate: X and Y are parallel.

T.6. $\|X \times Y\|^2 + (X \cdot Y)^2 = \|X\|^2 \|Y\|^2 (\sin^2\theta + \cos^2\theta) = \|X\|^2 \|Y\|^2.$

T.7. Using Theorem, 3.6(g),

$(X \times Y) \times Z + (Y \times Z) \times X + (Z \times X) \times Y = [(Z \cdot X)Y - (Z \cdot Y)X]$

$+ [(X \cdot Y)Z - (X \cdot Z)Y] + [(Y \cdot Z)X - (Y \cdot X)Z] = 0.$

Section 3.4, page 139

4. Properties (α), (a), (b), (c), (d) follow as for R^3.
    Regarding (β), (cx,y,z) is a triple of real numbers, so it lies in V.
    Regarding (g): $c \odot (d \odot (x,y,z)) = c \odot (dx,y,z) = (cdx,y,z) = (cd) \odot (x,y,z).$
    Regarding (h), $1 \odot (x,y,z) = (1 \cdot x,y,z) = (x,y,z).$

6. P is a vector space. Let $p(t)$ be a polynomial of degree n and $q(t)$ one of degree m, and $r = \max(n,m)$. Then inside the vector space P_r, addition of $p(t)$ and $q(t)$ is defined and multiplication of $p(t)$ by a scalar is defined, and these operations satisfy the vector space axioms. P_r is contained in P. Thus the additive inverse of $p(t)$, zero polynomial, etc. all lie in P. Hence P is a vector space.

8. Not a vector space; (e), (f) and (h) do not hold.

10. Vector space.

12. Not a vector space; (h) does not hold.

16. (a) and (b).

18. (a).

20. Each polynomial p(t) determines a real-valued function, namely
    r ⊢ p(r) for r ε R. Thus P is a subset of the vector space
    of all real-valued functions. Also, P is closed under vector
    addition and scalar multiplication. Thus it is a subspace of
    the function space.

22. Let Z_1 = aX + bY = (2a+4b,2b,3a-5b,-4a+b) and Z_2 = a'X + b'Y
    = (2a'+4b',2b',3a'-5b',-4a'+b') lie in W. Then
    $Z_1 + Z_2$ = (2(a+a')+4(b+b'),2(b+b'),3(a+a')-5(b+b')-4(a+a')+(b+b'))
    and cZ_1 = (2ac+4bc,2bc,3ac-5bc,-4ac+bc) both lie in W. By
    Theorem 3.8, W is a subspace.

24. (c).

26. (a), (b), (c), and (d).

T.1. cX = c(X+0) = cX + c0 = c0 + cX by Definition 1 (c), (e) and
     (a). Add the negative of cX to both sides of this equation to
     get 0 = c0 + cX + (-cX) = c0 + 0 = c0.

T.2. Since B≠0, A≠0. If AX=B has no solutions, then that empty set
     of solutions is not a vector space.
        Otherwise let X_0 be a solution. Then $A(2X_0) = 2(AX_0)$
     = 2B ≠ B since B ≠ 0. Thus $X_0 + X_0 = 2X_0$ is not a solution.
     Hence, the set of all solutions fails to be closed under either
     vector addition or scalar multiplication.

T.3. -(-X) is that unique vector which when added to -X gives 0.
     But X added to -X gives 0. Thus -(-X) = X.

T.4. Let W be a subspace of V, let X and Y be vectors in W, and
     a and b be scalars. Then aX ε W, bY ε W, and aX + bY ε W.
        Conversely, if aX + bY ε W for any X,Y in W and any
     scalars a,b, then in particular for a=b=1, X + Y ε W and for
     a=c, b=0, cX ε W. Thus W is a subspace by Theorem 3.8.

T.5. (cancellation): If X + Y = X + Z then

$$(-X) + (X+Y) = (-X) + (X+Z)$$
$$(-X + X) + Y = (-X + X) + Z$$
$$0 + Y = 0 + Z$$
$$Y = Z .$$

T.6. If $X \neq 0$ and $aX = bX$ then $(a-b)X = aX - bX = 0$. By Theorem 3.7(c), $a-b = 0$, $a = b$.

T.7. If W is a subspace, then for $X, Y \in W$, $X + Y$ and $c \cdot X$ lie in W by properties (α) and (β) of Definition 1.

Conversely, assume (α) and (β) of Theorem 3.8 hold. We must show that properties (a)-(h) in Definition 1 hold.

(a) since X,Y in W are a fortiori in V, $X + Y = Y + X$ by property (a) for V. Similarly for (b). By (β), for $c = 0$, $0 = 0 \cdot X$ lies in W. Again by (β), for $c = -1$, $-X = (-1)X$ lies in W. Thus (d) holds.

Finally (e), (f), (g), (h) follow for W because those properties hold for any vectors in V and any scalars.

T.8. We assume S is nonempty. Let $X = \sum_{i=1}^{k} a_i X_i$ and $Y = \sum_{i=1}^{k} b_i X_i$ be two vectors in span S. Then $X + Y = \sum_{i=1}^{k} (a_i + b_i) X_i$ and, for any c, $cX = \sum_{i=1}^{k} (ca_i) X_i$ are vectors in span S. Thus span S is a subspace of V.

T.9. W must be closed under vector addition and under multiplication of a vector by an arbitrary scalar. Thus, along with $X_1, X_2, \ldots, X_k$, W must contain $\sum_{i=1}^{k} a_i X_i$ for any set of coefficients $a_1, \ldots a_k$. Thus W contains span S.

Section 3.5, page 149

2. (a) and (c)
4. (a) and (b)
6. (a) no;   (b) no;   (c) no;   (d) yes.
8. (c) and (d).
10. (a) and (c).
12. (a) $X_2 = X_1 - 2X_3$

(c) $X_4 = 2X_1 + X_2 + X_3$.

14. (c) $p_1(t) = 3p_3(t) - 2p_2(t)$

    (d) $p_2(t) = 2p_1(t) + p_3(t)$.

T.1. If $c_1 E_1 + c_2 E_2 + \cdots + c_n E_n = (c_1, c_2, \cdots, c_n) = (0, 0, \cdots, 0) = 0$

    in R^n, then $c_1 = c_2 = \cdots = c_n = 0$.

T.2. (a) Since S_1 is linearly dependent, there are vectors
$X_1, X_2, \cdots, X_k$ in S_1 and constants $c_1, c_2, \cdots, c_k$ not all zero such
that $c_1 X_1 + c_2 X_2 + \cdots + c_k X_k = 0$. Those X_i's also lie in S_2,
hence S_2 is linearly dependent.

    (b) Suppose S_1 were linearly dependent, then by the theorem (a)
above, S_2 would be linearly dependent. Contradiction.

T.3. Assume that $S = \{X_1, X_2, \cdots, X_k\}$ is linearly dependent. Then
there are constants c_i not all zero such that

$$c_1 X_1 + c_2 X_2 + \cdots + c_k X_k = 0.$$

Let c_j be a nonzero coefficient. Then, solving the equation
for X_j,

$$X_j = -\frac{c_1}{c_j} X_1 - \frac{c_2}{c_j} X_2 - \frac{c_{j-1}}{c_j} X_{j-1} - \frac{c_{j+1}}{c_j} X_{j+1} - \cdots - \frac{c_k}{c_j} X_k.$$

    Conversely, if $X_j = d_1 X_1 + d_2 X_2 + \cdots + d_{j-1} X_{j-1} + d_{j+1} X_{j+1}$
$+ \cdots + d_k X_k$ for some coefficients d_i, then

$$d_1 X_1 + d_2 X_2 + \cdots + (-1) X_j + \cdots + d_k X_k = 0$$

and the set S is linearly dependent.

T.4. Suppose $c_1 Y_1 + c_2 Y_2 + c_3 Y_3 = c_1(X_1 + X_2 + X_3) + c_2(X_2 + X_3) + c_3 X_3$
$= c_1 X_1 + (c_1 + c_2) X_2 + (c_1 + c_2 + c_3) X_3 = 0$.
Since $\{X_1, X_2, X_3\}$ is linearly independent, $c_1 = 0$, $c_1 + c_2 = 0$
(and hence $c_2 = 0$), and $c_1 + c_2 + c_3 = 0$ (and hence $c_3 = 0$). Thus the
set $\{Y_1, Y_2, Y_3\}$ is linearly independent.

T.5. Suppose $\{X_1, X_2, X_3\}$ is linearly dependent. Then one of the X_j's is a linear combination of the preceding vectors in the list. It must be X_3 since $\{X_1, X_2\}$ is linearly independent. Thus X_3 belongs to span $\{X_1, X_2\}$. Contradiction.

T.6. Let $A_1, \ldots, A_r$ be the nonzero rows of the reduced row echelon form matrix A, and suppose

$$c_1 A_1 + c_2 A_2 + \cdots + c_r A_r = 0. \qquad (*)$$

For each j, $1 \le j \le r$, A_j is the only row with a nonzero entry in the column which holds the leading entry of that row. Thus, in the summation (*), c_j must $= 0$. Hence (*) is the trivial dependence relation, and the A_i are linearly independent.

T.7. Let $Y_i = \sum_{j=1}^{k} a_{ij} X_j$ for $i = 1, 2, \ldots, m$. Then

$$Z = \sum_{i=1}^{m} b_i Y_i = \sum_{i=1}^{m} b_i \sum_{j=1}^{k} a_{ij} X_j$$

$$= \sum_{j=1}^{k} \left(\sum_{i=1}^{m} b_i a_{ij} \right) X_j$$

is a linear combination of the vectors X_j in S.

T.8. Consider in $R = R^1$ the dependent subset $S_2 = \{1, \pi\}$. (1 and π are two vectors (real numbers) in R^1.) The subset $S_1 = \{1\}$ is linearly independent while the subset $S_1' = S_2 = \{1, \pi\}$ is linearly dependent.

T.9. Similar to T.8.

2. (c).

4. (d).

6. If

$$c_1\begin{bmatrix} 1 & 1 \\ 0 & 0 \end{bmatrix} + c_2\begin{bmatrix} 0 & 0 \\ 1 & 1 \end{bmatrix} + c_3\begin{bmatrix} 1 & 0 \\ 0 & 1 \end{bmatrix} + c_4\begin{bmatrix} 0 & 1 \\ 1 & 1 \end{bmatrix} = \begin{bmatrix} 0 & 0 \\ 0 & 0 \end{bmatrix},$$

then $\begin{bmatrix} c_1 + c_3 & c_1 + c_4 \\ c_2 + c_4 & c_2 + c_3 + c_4 \end{bmatrix} = \begin{bmatrix} 0 & 0 \\ 0 & 0 \end{bmatrix}$. The first three

entries imply $c_3 = -c_1 = c_4 = -c_2$. The fourth entry gives
$c_2 - c_2 - c_2 = -c_2 = 0$. Thus $c_i = 0$ for $i = 1,2,3,4$. Hence the
set of four matrices is linearly independent. By Theorem 3.14,
it is a basis.

8. (a), $5t^2 - 3t + 8 = 5(t^2 + t) - 8(t-1)$; and

   (c), $5t^2 - 3t + 8 = -3(t^2 + t) + 8(t^2 - 1)$.

10. Possible answer $\{X_1, X_2, X_3\}$; dim W = 3.

12. Possible answer $\{\cos^2 t, \sin^2 t\}$; dim W = 2.

14. (a) 3;   (b) 2;   (c) 3;   (d) 2.

16. (a) 2;   (b) 3;   (c) 3;   (d) 3.

18. (a) Possible answer $\{(1,0,2), (1,0,0), (0,1,0)\}$,

    (b) Possible answer $\{(1,0,2), (0,1,3), (1,0,0)\}$.

20. Possible answer $\left\{ \begin{bmatrix} -3 \\ 0 \\ 1 \\ 1 \\ 0 \end{bmatrix}, \begin{bmatrix} -2 \\ 1 \\ 0 \\ 0 \\ 0 \end{bmatrix} \right\}$;   dim W = 2.

22. Possible answer $\left\{ \begin{bmatrix} -1 \\ 1 \\ 0 \\ 1 \\ 0 \end{bmatrix}, \begin{bmatrix} -2 \\ 1/2 \\ 0 \\ 0 \\ 1 \end{bmatrix} \right\}$;   dim W = 2.

24. The solution space is $\left\{ \begin{bmatrix} 0 \\ 0 \\ 0 \end{bmatrix} \right\}$; there is no basis; the
dimension is 0.

T.1. If $S = \{X_1, X_2, \cdots, X_m\}$ is linearly independent, then it is a basis for W. Otherwise some X_j in S is a linear combination of the remaining vectors. Let S_1 be the set S with X_j deleted. Then S_1 spans W. Repeat the above argument applied to S_1: either S_1 is a basis, or there is some smaller subset S_2 which spans W. Since $W \neq 0$, eventually this repetition leads to a nonempty basis for W which is a subset of the original set S.

T.2. Since the largest number of vectors in any linearly independent set is m, dim V = m. The result follows from Theorem 3.14.

T.3. Let dim V = n and let X_1 be a nonzero vector in the nonzero subspace W. If $\{X_1\}$ spans W, then it is a basis for W and $1 = \dim W \leq n$. Otherwise chose X_2 in W such that $\{X_1, X_2\}$ is linearly independent. If $\{X_1, X_2\}$ spans W, then it is a basis for W. Otherwise chose X_3 in W such that $\{X_1, X_2, X_3\}$ is linearly independent. Eventually we reach a set $\{X_1, X_2, \cdots, X_m\}$ of m vectors which is a basis for W. Since that is a linearly independent set contained in V, and dim V = n, we have $m \leq n$.

T.4. By Theorem 3.12, any linearly independent set T of vectors in V has at most n elements. Thus a set of n+1 vectors must be linearly dependent.

T.5. Suppose a set S of n-1 vectors in V spans V. By Theorem 3.11, some subset of S would be a basis for V. Thus dim V $\leq$ n-1. Contradiction.

T.6. Let $S = \{Y_1, Y_2, \cdots, Y_k\}$ be a linearly independent set of vectors in V and let $\{X_1, \cdots, X_n\}$ be a basis for V (V is finite dimensional). Let $S_1 = \{Y_1, Y_2, \cdots, Y_k, X_1, X_2, \cdots, X_n\}$. S_1 spans V (since the subset $\{X_1, X_2, \cdots, X_n\}$ does). If S_1 is linearly independent, then it is a basis for V which contains S. Otherwise some vector in S_1 is a linear combination of the preceding vectors (Theorem 3.9). That vector cannot be one of the Y_i's since S is linearly independent. So it is one of the X_j's. Delete it to form a new set S_2 with one fewer element than S_1 which also spans V. Either S_2 is a basis or else another X_j can be deleted. After a finite number of steps we arrive at a set S_p which is a basis for V and which contains the given set S.

T.7.   (a) By Theorem 3.13, there is a basis T for V which contains
       $S = \{X_1, X_2, \cdots, X_n\}$. Since dim V = n, T cannot have more
       vectors than S. Thus T = S.
       (b) By Theorem 3.11, some subset T of S is a basis for V.
       Since dim V = n, T has n elements. Thus T = S.

T.8.   Let $S = \{X_1, X_2, \cdots, X_m\}$ be a basis for W. By Theorem 3.13,
       there is a basis T for V which contains the linearly indepen-
       dent set S. Since dim W = m = dim V, T must have m elements.
       Thus T=S and V=W.

T.9.   The zero subspace {0}, the entire space R^3, all lines through
       the origin, and all planes through the origin.

T.10. If X is a linear combination of $\{X_1, X_2, \cdots, X_n\}$:

$$X = d_1 X_1 + d_2 X_2 + \cdots + d_n X_n, \quad \text{then}$$

$$X = \frac{d_1}{c}(cX_1) + d_2 X_2 + \cdots + d_n X_n \text{ and so X is a linear}$$

combination of $\{cX_1, X_2, \cdots, X_n\}$. Similarly any vector which
is a linear combination of the second set

$$X = d_1(cX_1) + d_2 X_2 + \cdots + d_n X_n,$$

is a linear combination of the first set: $X = (d_1 c)X_1 + \cdots + d_n X_n$.
Thus the two sets span V. Since the second set has n
elements, it is also a basis for V.

T.11. The set $T = \{Y_1, Y_2, Y_3\}$ is a set of three vectors in the three
       dimensional vector space V. One may solve for the X's in
       terms of the Y's:

$$X_3 = Y_3$$
$$X_2 = Y_2 - X_3 = Y_2 - Y_3$$
$$X_1 = Y_1 - X_2 - X_3 = Y_1 - (Y_2 - Y_3) - Y_3 = Y_1 - Y_2$$

Thus $S = \{X_1, X_2, X_3\}$ is contained in span T and so V = span S
is contained in span T. Hence T is a basis for V.

2. Possible answer: $\{(1,0,0,0), (0,1,0,0), (0,0,1,0), (0,0,0,1)\}$.

4. Possible answer:

$$\left\{ \begin{bmatrix} 1 \\ 0 \\ 0 \\ 0 \end{bmatrix}, \begin{bmatrix} 0 \\ 1 \\ 0 \\ 0 \end{bmatrix}, \begin{bmatrix} 0 \\ 0 \\ 1 \\ 0 \end{bmatrix}, \begin{bmatrix} 0 \\ 0 \\ 0 \\ 1 \end{bmatrix} \right\}.$$

6. 5.

8. 4.

10. 2.

12. 3.

14. The 5 rows of A span a row space of dimension rank A, which is at most 3. Thus the 5 rows are linearly dependent.

16. Nonsingular.

18. Yes, linearly independent.

20. Only the trivial solution.

22. Only the trivial solution.

24. Has a solution.

26. Has no solution.

T.1. Let the matrix in reduced row echelon form have r nonzero rows $B_1, B_2, \cdots, B_r$. Clearly those r nonzero rows span its row space. Suppose next that some linear combination

$\sum\limits_{k=1}^{r} c_k B_k$ equals 0. If the ith row has its leading entry in the jth column, then since all other rows have entry 0 in the jth column, the jth coordinate of $\sum c_k B_k$ is $c_i \cdot 1$, which must $= 0$. Thus $c_i = 0$ for $i = 1, \cdots, r$. Thus the r nonzero rows are linearly independent, and hence constitute a basis for the row space.

T.2. Rank $A = n$ if and only if A is nonsingular if and only if det $A \neq 0$.

T.3. $S = \{X_1, \cdots, X_n\}$ is linearly independent if and only if A has rank n if and only if $|A| \neq 0$.

T.4. Let $A_1, A_2, \ldots, A_n$ be the columns of the matrix A. If the system AX = 0 has a nontrivial solution $X = (c_1, c_2, \ldots, c_n)^T$, then from the definition of matrix product,

$A_1c_1 + A_2c_2 + \cdots + A_nc_n = 0$ and the columns are linearly dependent. For the converse, reverse the direction of the argument.

T.5. n = rank A = column rank A implies the n columns of A are linearly independent.

T.6. If the rows of A are linearly independent, n = rank A = column rank A and the columns span the entire space R^n.

Section 3.8, page 179

2. (a).

4. $\left\{ \left(\dfrac{1}{\sqrt{5}}, 0, \dfrac{2}{\sqrt{5}} \right), \left(\dfrac{-4}{3\sqrt{5}}, \dfrac{5}{3\sqrt{5}}, \dfrac{2}{3\sqrt{5}} \right) \right\}$.

6. $\left\{ \left(\dfrac{1}{\sqrt{3}}, \dfrac{1}{\sqrt{3}}, \dfrac{-1}{\sqrt{3}}, 0 \right), \left(\dfrac{-2}{\sqrt{33}}, \dfrac{4}{\sqrt{33}}, \dfrac{2}{\sqrt{33}}, \dfrac{3}{\sqrt{33}} \right), \left(\dfrac{4}{\sqrt{110}}, \dfrac{3}{\sqrt{110}}, \dfrac{7}{\sqrt{110}}, \dfrac{-6}{\sqrt{110}} \right) \right.$

8. $\left\{ \left(\dfrac{1}{\sqrt{3}}, \dfrac{1}{\sqrt{3}}, \dfrac{1}{\sqrt{3}} \right), \left(\dfrac{-2}{\sqrt{6}}, \dfrac{1}{\sqrt{6}}, \dfrac{1}{\sqrt{6}} \right), \left(0, \dfrac{-1}{\sqrt{2}}, \dfrac{1}{\sqrt{2}} \right) \right\}$.

10. Possible answer $\left\{ (0,0,1), \left(\dfrac{1}{\sqrt{2}}, \dfrac{1}{\sqrt{2}}, 0 \right), \left(\dfrac{-1}{\sqrt{2}}, \dfrac{1}{\sqrt{2}}, 0 \right) \right\}$.

12. $\dfrac{5}{\sqrt{2}} \left(\dfrac{1}{\sqrt{2}}, \dfrac{1}{\sqrt{2}} \right) + \dfrac{1}{\sqrt{2}} \left(\dfrac{-1}{\sqrt{2}}, \dfrac{1}{\sqrt{2}} \right) = (2,3)$.

14. $Z = \left(-\dfrac{1}{5}, 2, -\dfrac{2}{5} \right)$, $Y = \left(\dfrac{6}{5}, 0, -\dfrac{3}{5} \right)$

16. $3/\sqrt{5}$

T.1. $E_i \cdot E_j = 0$ for $i \neq j$ and 1 for $i = j$.

T.2. An orthonormal set in R^n is an orthogonal set of nonzero vectors. The result follows from Theorem 3.18.

T.4. Let $X = c_1 X_1 + \cdots + c_n X_n$ be the expression for X in terms of the basis S. Then

$$X \cdot X_i = \left(\sum_{j=1}^{n} c_j X_j \right) \cdot X_i = \sum_{j=1}^{n} c_j (X_j \cdot X_i) = c_i$$

for $1 \le i \le n$.

Review Exercises, page 181

2. No.   4. Yes.   6. Yes.   8. 2

10. Possible answer: $\{(1,2,-1,2), (0,-1,3,-6), (1,-1,0,-2)\}$.

12. $\lambda \ne -1, 0, 1$

14. Possible answer: $\left\{ \left(\frac{1}{\sqrt{2}}, 0, 0, \frac{-1}{\sqrt{2}} \right), \left(\frac{1}{\sqrt{6}}, \frac{-2}{\sqrt{6}}, 0, \frac{1}{\sqrt{6}} \right), \left(\frac{1}{\sqrt{3}}, \frac{1}{\sqrt{3}}, 0, \frac{1}{\sqrt{3}} \right) \right\}$

CHAPTER 4

Section 4.1, page 190

2. (b).

4. (a) (2,15);   (b) $(2a + 3b + 2c, -4a - 5b + 3c)$.

6. (a) Reflection about the y-axis;
   (b) Reflection about the origin;
   (c) Rotate counterclockwise through $\frac{\pi}{2}$.

8. (a) $2t^3 - 5t^2 + 2t + 3$;   (b) $at^3 + bt^2 + at + c$.

10. $L(f+g) = \int_0^1 (f(x) + g(x))dx = \int_0^1 f(x)dx + \int_0^1 g(x)dx = L(f) + L(g)$,

    $L(\lambda f) = \int_0^1 (\lambda f(x))dx = \lambda \int_0^1 f(x)dx = \lambda L(f)$.

12. (a) 160, 61, 123, 47, 43, 17, 102, 40;
    (b) OF COURSE.

T.1. $L(X+Y) = A(X+Y) = AX + AY = L(X) + L(Y)$, $L(cX) = A(cX) = c(AX)$
$= cL(X)$.

T.2. $L(c_1X_1 + c_2X_2 + \cdots + c_kX_k) = L(c_1X_1) + L(c_2X_2 + \cdots + c_kX_k)$
$= c_1L(X_1) + L(c_2X_2) + L(c_3X_3 + \cdots + c_kX_k) = \cdots$
$= c_1L(X_1) + c_2L(X_2) + \cdots + c_kL(X_k)$.

T.3. $L(X-Y) = L(X + (-1)Y) = L(X) + (-1)L(Y) = L(X) - L(Y)$.

T.4. If L is a linear transformation then

$$L(aX + bY) = aL(X) + bL(Y) \qquad (*)$$

by Theorem 4.1. Conversely if equation (*) holds for
any a and b and vectors X and Y, then in particular it
holds for a=b=1, which gives (a) of the definition of
linear transformation, and for a=c, b=0, which gives (b)
of that definition.

T.5. (a) $\operatorname{tr}(A+B) = \sum_{i=1}^{n}(a_{ii}+b_{ii}) = \sum_{i=1}^{n}a_{ii} + \sum_{i=1}^{n}b_{ii} = \operatorname{tr}(A) + \operatorname{tr}(B)$;

(b) $\operatorname{tr}(cA) = \sum_{i=1}^{n}(ca_{ii}) = c\sum_{i=1}^{n}a_{ii} = c\operatorname{tr}(A)$.

T.6. Yes. (a) $L(A+B) = (A+B)^T = A^T + B^T = L(A) + L(B)$;

(b) $L(cA) = (cA)^T = cA^T = cL(A)$.

T.7. No. Let $n = 2$, $A = \begin{bmatrix} 1 & 0 \\ 0 & 0 \end{bmatrix}$, $B = \begin{bmatrix} 0 & 0 \\ 0 & 1 \end{bmatrix}$.

Then $L(A+B) = L\left(\begin{bmatrix} 1 & 0 \\ 0 & 1 \end{bmatrix}\right) = \begin{bmatrix} 1 & 0 \\ 0 & 1 \end{bmatrix} \neq 0 + 0 = L(A) + L(B)$.

2. (a) No;   (b) Yes;   (c) Yes;   (d) No;

(e) $\left\{\begin{bmatrix} -2r \\ r \end{bmatrix}\right\}$, r = any real number

(f) Possible answer: $\left\{\begin{bmatrix} 1 \\ 2 \end{bmatrix}\right\}$.

4. (a) Possible answer: $\{(1,-1,-1,1)\}$;

(b) Possible answer: $\{(1,0,0),\ (0,1,0),\ (0,0,1)\}$;

(c) dim (ker L) + dim (range L) = 1 + 3 = 4 = dim V.

6. (a) No;   (b) 2.

8. (a) ker L = {0}, it has no basis;

(b) Possible answer $\{(1,1,0),(-1,2,0),(0,0,1)\}$.

10.(a) Possible answer $\left\{\begin{bmatrix} 1 \\ -8/3 \\ 4/3 \\ 1 \end{bmatrix}\right\}$;

(b) Possible answer $\left\{\begin{bmatrix} 1 \\ 2 \\ 1 \\ 4 \end{bmatrix}, \begin{bmatrix} 2 \\ 1 \\ 0 \\ 1 \end{bmatrix}, \begin{bmatrix} 1 \\ -1 \\ 0 \\ -1 \end{bmatrix}\right\}$.

12. (a) No; (b) No; (c) Yes; (d) No;

(e) Possible answer: $\{t+1,\ t^3+t^2\}$;

(f) Possible answer: $\{t^3,t\}$

14. (a) Possible answer: $\{t^2 - \frac{1}{3},\ t - \frac{1}{2}\}$;

(b) Possible answer: $\{1\}$.

16. (a) 7; (b) 5.

18. 2.

T.1. By Theorem 4.7 and assumption that dim V = dim W,
dim(ker L) + dim(range L) = dim W.

(a) If L is one-to-one, dim(range L) = dim W, so L is onto.
(b) If L is onto, dim(ker L) = 0, so L is one-to-one.

T.2. If Y lies in the range of L, then Y = AX for some X in R^n, and Y is a linear combination of columns of A. Thus Y lies in the column space of A. Conversely, let $X = E_j$ (jth natural basis vector), then the jth column of A lies in the range of L. This holds for $1 \le j \le n$. Thus the column space of A is contained in the range of L.

T.3. L is one-to-one if and only if ker L = {0} if and only if dim(range A) = n if and only if dim(column space of A) = n if and only if rank A = n if and only if $|A| \ne 0$.

T.4. Let Y be any vector in range L. Then there exists a vector X in V such that L(X) = Y. Next there exist scalars $c_1, \cdots, c_k$ such that $X = c_1 X_1 + \cdots + c_k X_k$. Thus $Y = L(c_1 X_1 + \cdots + c_k X_k) = c_1 L(X_1) + \cdots + c_k L(X_k)$. Hence $\{L(X_1), L(X_2), \cdots, L(X_k)\}$ spans range L.

T.5. (a) dim(ker L) + dim(range L) = dim V, dim(ker L) $\ge$ 0; thus dim(range L) $\le$ dim V;
(b) If L is onto, then range L = W and the result follows from part (a).

T.6. If $T = \{L(X_1), L(X_2), \cdots, L(X_n)\}$ is linearly independent, and if $c_1 X_1 + c_2 X_2 + \cdots + c_n X_n = 0$, then $c_1 L(X_1) + c_2 L(X_2) + \cdots + c_n L(X_n) = L(c_1 X_1 + \cdots + c_n X_n) = L(0) = 0$, which implies $c_1 = c_2 = \cdots = c_n = 0$. Thus $\{X_1, X_2, \cdots, X_n\}$ is linearly independent.

T.7. L is one-to-one if and only if dim ker L = 0 if and only if dim(range L) = dim V.

T.8. Let L be one-to-one and let $S = \{X_1, \cdots, X_k\}$ be a linearly independent set of vectors in V. Suppose that $\{L(X_1), L(X_2), \cdots, L(X_k)\}$ is linearly dependent. Then there exist constants $c_1, c_2, \cdots, c_k$, not all zero, so that

$$c_1 L(X_1) + c_2 L(X_2) + \cdots + c_k L(X_k) = 0$$

or

$$L(c_1 X_1 + c_2 X_2 + \cdots + c_k X_k) = 0 = L(0).$$

Since L is one-to-one, we have $c_1 X_1 + c_2 X_2 + \cdots + c_k X_k = 0$, which implies that S is linearly dependent, a contradiction.

T.9. The "only if" portion follows from Exercise T.8. If the image of a basis for V is a basis for W, then range L has dimension = dim W = dim V, and hence ker L has dimension 0, so L is one-to-one.

Section 4.3, page 212

2. (a) $\begin{bmatrix} 0 \\ 2 \\ 1 \end{bmatrix}$; (b) $\begin{bmatrix} 2 \\ -1 \\ 1 \end{bmatrix}$; (c) $\begin{bmatrix} 3 \\ -1 \\ -1 \end{bmatrix}$; (d) $\begin{bmatrix} 2 \\ 0 \\ -1 \end{bmatrix}$.

4. (a) $\begin{bmatrix} 2 \\ 1 \end{bmatrix}$; (b) $\begin{bmatrix} -1 \\ -1 \end{bmatrix}$; (c) $\begin{bmatrix} 1 \\ 0 \end{bmatrix}$; (d) $\begin{bmatrix} -1 \\ 3 \end{bmatrix}$.

6. (a) $\begin{bmatrix} 1 & 2 \\ 2 & -1 \end{bmatrix}$; (b) $\begin{bmatrix} 1 & -1/2 \\ 1 & 3/4 \end{bmatrix}$; (c) $\begin{bmatrix} 3 & 2 \\ -4 & 4 \end{bmatrix}$; (d) $\begin{bmatrix} -2 & 2 \\ 1/2 & 2 \end{bmatrix}$;

(e) $\begin{bmatrix} 5 \\ 0 \end{bmatrix}$.

8. (a) $\begin{bmatrix} 1 & 2 & 1 \\ 2 & -1 & 0 \\ 0 & 2 & 1 \end{bmatrix}$; (b) $\begin{bmatrix} 1 & 2 & 1 \\ 2 & -1 & 0 \\ -3 & 1 & 0 \end{bmatrix}$; (c) $\begin{bmatrix} 2 & 3 & 1 \\ 2 & -1 & 0 \\ 1 & 3 & 1 \end{bmatrix}$;

(d) $\begin{bmatrix} 2 & 3 & 1 \\ 2 & -1 & 0 \\ -3 & -1 & 0 \end{bmatrix}$; (e) $\begin{bmatrix} 1 \\ 1 \\ 0 \end{bmatrix}$.

10. (a) $L(X) = \begin{bmatrix} 1 & 1 \\ 1 & -1 \\ 1 & 2 \end{bmatrix} X$, (b) $[L(X)]_{T'} = \begin{bmatrix} 1 & -1/3 \\ 0 & 2/3 \\ -1 & 4/3 \end{bmatrix} [X]_{S'}$;

(c) $\begin{bmatrix} -1 \\ 5 \\ -4 \end{bmatrix}$.

12. (a) $\begin{bmatrix} 1 & 0 \\ 0 & 1 \\ 0 & 1 \end{bmatrix}$; (b) $\begin{bmatrix} 1 & 1 \\ 1/2 & 1/2 \\ 1/2 & -3/2 \end{bmatrix}$; (c) $-3t^2 + 3t + 3$.

14. $\begin{bmatrix} 3 & 2 \\ -2 & 1 \end{bmatrix}$.

16. (a) $[L(X_1)]_T = \begin{bmatrix} 1 \\ -1 \end{bmatrix}$, $[L(X_2)]_T = \begin{bmatrix} 2 \\ 1 \end{bmatrix}$, $[L(X_3)]_T = \begin{bmatrix} 1 \\ 0 \end{bmatrix}$;

(b) $L(X_1) = \begin{bmatrix} 0 \\ 3 \end{bmatrix}$, $L(X_2) = \begin{bmatrix} 3 \\ 3 \end{bmatrix}$, $L(X_3) = \begin{bmatrix} 1 \\ 2 \end{bmatrix}$; (c) $\begin{bmatrix} -3 \\ 3 \\ 1 \end{bmatrix}$.

18. $\begin{bmatrix} 1 & 0 \\ 0 & -1 \end{bmatrix}$.

T.1. If $Y = L(X)$ for some X in V, and if $X = a_1 X_1 + \cdots + a_n X_n$,
then

$$Y = L(X) = L(\sum_{j=1}^{n} a_j X_j) = \sum_{j=1}^{n} a_j L(X_j)$$

$$= \begin{bmatrix} c_{11} \\ c_{21} \\ \cdot \\ \cdot \\ \cdot \\ c_{m1} \end{bmatrix} a_1 + \begin{bmatrix} c_{12} \\ c_{22} \\ \cdot \\ \cdot \\ \cdot \\ c_{m2} \end{bmatrix} a_2 + \cdots + \begin{bmatrix} c_{1n} \\ c_{2n} \\ \cdot \\ \cdot \\ \cdot \\ c_{mn} \end{bmatrix} a_n$$

$$= \begin{bmatrix} c_{11} & c_{12} & \cdots & c_{1n} \\ c_{21} & c_{22} & \cdots & c_{2n} \\ \cdot & \cdot & & \cdot \\ \cdot & \cdot & & \cdot \\ \cdot & \cdot & & \cdot \\ c_{m1} & c_{m2} & \cdots & c_{mn} \end{bmatrix} \begin{bmatrix} a_1 \\ a_2 \\ \cdot \\ \cdot \\ \cdot \\ a_n \end{bmatrix} = A[X]_S .$$

Regarding the uniqueness of the matrix A, for each $1 \le j \le n$,
the jth column of A is uniquely determined, since for
$X = X_j = 0 \cdot X_1 + \cdots + 1 \cdot X_j + \cdots + 0 \cdot X_n$; $[Y]_T = A \cdot E_j$
= the jth column of A.

T.2. Let $S = \{X_1, \cdots, X_n\}$. For each j, $1 \le j \le n$,
$I(X_j) = X_j = 0 \cdot X_1 + \cdots + 1 \cdot X_j + \cdots + 0 \cdot X_n$. Thus the jth column
of the matrix representing the identity transformation is E_j.
Hence the entire matrix is I_n.

T.3. Let $S = \{X_1, \cdots, X_n\}$ be a basis for V, $T = \{Y_1, \cdots, Y_m\}$ a basis for W. Then $0(X_j) = O_w = 0 \cdot Y_1 + \cdots + 0 \cdot Y_m$.

If A is the matrix of the zero transformation with respect to these bases, then the jth column of A is 0. Thus A is the m×n zero matrix.

T.4. Let $S = \{X_1, \cdots, X_n\}$ be a basis for V. Then $L(X_j) = cX_j$ $= 0 \cdot X_1 + \cdots + cX_j + \cdots + 0X_n$. If A is the matrix of L with respect to S, then the jth column of A is cE_j, where E_j is the jth natural basis vector. Thus $A = cI_n$.

Review Exercises, page 215

2. $L(X+Y) = (X+Y) \cdot X_0$
$= X \cdot X_0 + Y \cdot X_0$
$= L(X) + L(Y)$

and

$L(cX) = (cX) \cdot X_0$
$c(X \cdot X_0) = cL(X)$.

4. Possible answer: $\{2t^2 + t+1\}$;   (b) No.

6. 2 .   8. (a) $\begin{bmatrix} 1 & 0 & 2 \\ 2 & 1 & 0 \\ -2 & 0 & -1 \end{bmatrix}$;   (b) $4t^2 - 4t + 1$.

10. $\begin{bmatrix} 0 & 0 & 0 & 0 \\ 3 & 0 & 0 & 0 \\ 0 & 2 & 0 & 0 \\ 0 & 0 & 1 & 0 \end{bmatrix}$.

CHAPTER 5

Section 5.1, page 234

2. $\lambda^2 - 5\lambda + 7$.

4. $f(\lambda) = \lambda^3$; $\lambda_1 = \lambda_2 = \lambda_3 = 0$; $x_1 = \begin{bmatrix} 1 \\ 0 \\ 0 \end{bmatrix}$, $x_2 = \begin{bmatrix} 2 \\ 0 \\ 0 \end{bmatrix}$,

$x_3 = \begin{bmatrix} 3 \\ 0 \\ 0 \end{bmatrix}$.

6. $f(\lambda) = \lambda^2 - 2\lambda = \lambda(\lambda - 2)$; $\lambda_1 = 0$, $\lambda_2 = 2$;

$x_1 = \begin{bmatrix} 1 \\ -1 \end{bmatrix}$, $x_2 = \begin{bmatrix} 1 \\ 1 \end{bmatrix}$.

8. $f(\lambda) = \lambda^3 - 7\lambda^2 + 14\lambda - 8$; $\lambda_1 = 1$, $\lambda_2 = 2$, $\lambda_3 = 4$;

$x_1 = \begin{bmatrix} -1 \\ 1 \\ 1 \end{bmatrix}$, $x_2 = \begin{bmatrix} 1 \\ 0 \\ 0 \end{bmatrix}$, $x_3 = \begin{bmatrix} 7 \\ -4 \\ 2 \end{bmatrix}$.

10. $f(\lambda) = (\lambda - 2)(\lambda + 1)(\lambda - 3)$; $\lambda_1 = 2$, $\lambda_2 = -1$, $\lambda_3 = 3$;

$x_1 = \begin{bmatrix} 1 \\ 1 \\ -4 \end{bmatrix}$, $x_2 = \begin{bmatrix} 0 \\ 1 \\ -1 \end{bmatrix}$, $x_3 = \begin{bmatrix} 0 \\ 0 \\ 1 \end{bmatrix}$.

12. Diagonalizable; $\lambda_1 = -3$, $\lambda_2 = 2$.

14. Diagonalizable; $\lambda_1 = 0$, $\lambda_2 = 2$, $\lambda_3 = 3$.

16. Not diagonalizable; $\lambda_1 = \lambda_2 = \lambda_3 = 3$.

18. $P = \begin{bmatrix} 1 & 0 & 1 \\ 0 & -2 & 0 \\ 0 & 1 & 1 \end{bmatrix}$; $\lambda_1 = 1$, $\lambda_2 = 1$, $\lambda_3 = 3$.

20. $P = \begin{bmatrix} 1 & 1 \\ -1 & -2 \end{bmatrix}$; $\lambda_1 = 1$, $\lambda_2 = 2$.

22. Basis for eigenspace associated with $\lambda_1 = \lambda_2 = 2$ is

$$\left\{ \begin{bmatrix} 1 \\ 0 \\ 0 \end{bmatrix}, \begin{bmatrix} 0 \\ 0 \\ 1 \end{bmatrix} \right\} .$$

Basis for eigenspace associated with $\lambda_3 = 1$ is $\left\{ \begin{bmatrix} 3 \\ -1 \\ 0 \end{bmatrix} \right\}$.

24. $\begin{bmatrix} 512 & 0 \\ 0 & -512 \end{bmatrix}$ 26. $\begin{bmatrix} 8 \\ 2 \\ 1 \end{bmatrix}$.

T.1. (a) $A = P^{-1}AP$ for $P = I_n$,

(b) If $B = P^{-1}AP$, then $A = PBP^{-1}$ and so A is similar to B,

(c) If $B = P^{-1}AP$ and $C = Q^{-1}BQ$ then $C = Q^{-1}P^{-1}APQ$

$= (PQ)^{-1} A(PQ)$ with PQ nonsingular.

T.2. Let X, Y be vectors in S and c a scalar. Then
$A(X + Y) = AX + AY = \lambda X + \lambda Y = \lambda(X + Y)$ and $A(cX) = c(AX)$
$= c\lambda X = \lambda(cX)$. Thus both $X + Y$ and cX are either eigenvectors associated with λ or else 0. Thus both lie in S and
S is a subspace.

T.3. Suppose $B = P^{-1}AP$ for some nonsingular matrix P. The
characteristic polynomial of B is

$|\lambda I_n - B| = |\lambda I_n - P^{-1}AP| = |P^{-1}(\lambda I_n - A)P|$

$= |P^{-1}| \cdot |\lambda I_n - A| \cdot |P| = |\lambda I_n - A|$ since the numbers $|P^{-1}|$

and $|P|$ are reciprocals. Thus A and B have the same

characteristic polynomials.

T.4. $(\lambda I_n - A)$ is a triangular matrix, whose determinant is the
product of its diagonal elements:
$$(\lambda - a_{11})(\lambda - a_{22}) \cdots (\lambda - a_{nn}).$$

T.5. $|\lambda I_n - A^T| = |(\lambda I_n - A)^T| = |\lambda I_n - A|$. Associated eigenvectors need not be the same. (But the dimensions of the eigenspace associated with λ, for A and for A^T, are equal.)

T.6. $A^k X = A^{k-1}(AX) = A^{k-1}(\lambda X) = \lambda A^{k-1} X = \cdots = \lambda^k X$.

T.7. If A is nilpotent and $A^k = 0$, and if λ is an eigenvalue for A with associated eigenvector X, then $0 = A^k = A^k X = \lambda^k X$ implies $\lambda^k = 0$ (since $X \neq 0$), so $\lambda = 0$.

T.8. (a) The product of the (complex) roots of a polynomial $f(\lambda)$ with leading coefficient 1 is $(-1)^n$ times the constant term of the polynomial. The constant term of the characteristic polynomial $f(\lambda) = |\lambda I_n - A|$ is $f(0) = |-A| = (-1)^n |A|$. Thus $|A|$ equals the product of the roots.

(b) A is singular if and only if for some nonzero vector X, $AX = 0$, if and only if 0 is an eigenvalue of A.
   Alternately, A is singular if and only if $|A| = 0$, if and only if (by (a)) 0 is a real root of the characteristic polynomial of A.

T.9. If $AX = \lambda X$, $\lambda \neq 0$, then $\lambda^{-1} X = \lambda^{-1} A^{-1} AX = \lambda A^{-1}(\lambda X) = \lambda^{-1} \lambda A^{-1} X = A^{-1} X$, and thus λ^{-1} is an eigenvalue of A^{-1} with associated eigenvector X.

T.10. Necessary and sufficient conditions are: $)a - d)^2 + 4bc > 0$ for $b = c = 0$. For the characteristic polynomial of

$$A = \begin{bmatrix} a & b \\ c & d \end{bmatrix} \quad \text{is} \quad f(\lambda) = \begin{vmatrix} \lambda - a & -b \\ -c & \lambda - d \end{vmatrix}.$$

$= \lambda^2 + \lambda(-a - d) + ad - bc$. Then $f(\lambda)$ has real roots if and only if $(a + d)^2 - 4(ad - bc)^2 = (a - d)^2 + 4bc \geq 0$. If $(a - d)^2 + 4bc > 0$ then the eigenvalues are distinct and we can diagonalize. On the other hand, if $(a - d)^2 + 4bc = 0$ then the two eigenvalues λ_1 and λ_2 are equal and we have $\lambda_1 = \lambda_2 = \frac{a + d}{2}$. To find associated eigenvectors we are then solving the homogeneous system

$$\begin{bmatrix} \frac{d - a}{2} & -b \\ -c & \frac{a - d}{2} \end{bmatrix} \begin{bmatrix} x_1 \\ x_2 \end{bmatrix} = \begin{bmatrix} 0 \\ 0 \end{bmatrix}.$$

In this case A is diagonalizable if and only if the solution
space has dimension = 2; that is, if and only if the rank of
the coefficient matrix = 0, thus, if and only if b = c = 0
so that A is already diagonal.

T.11. We have $BA = A^{-1}(AB)A$, so AB and BA are similar. By Exercise
T.3, AB and BA have the same characterisitic polynomials and
thus the same eigenvalues.

T.12. (a) If $P^{-1}AP = D$ a diagonal matrix, then $P^TA^T(P^{-1})^T$

$= (P^{-1}AP)^T = D^T$ is diagonal, and $P^T = ((P^{-1})^T)^{-1}$, so A^T

is similar to a diagonal matrix,

(b) $P^{-1}A^kP = (P^{-1}AP)^k = D^k$ is diagonal.

Section 5.2, page 245

2. (a) $A^{-1} = A^T = \begin{bmatrix} 1 & 0 & 0 \\ 0 & \cos\theta & -\sin\theta \\ 0 & \sin\theta & \cos\theta \end{bmatrix}$; (b) $B^{-1} = B$.

6. $A = \begin{bmatrix} 1/\sqrt{2} & -1/\sqrt{2} \\ 1/\sqrt{2} & 1/\sqrt{2} \end{bmatrix}$.

8. $\begin{bmatrix} 0 & 0 & 0 \\ 0 & 1 & 0 \\ 0 & 0 & -1 \end{bmatrix}$; $P = \begin{bmatrix} 0 & 1/\sqrt{2} & 1/\sqrt{2} \\ 1 & 0 & 0 \\ 0 & 1/\sqrt{2} & -1/\sqrt{2} \end{bmatrix}$.

10. $\begin{bmatrix} 0 & 0 & 0 & 0 \\ 0 & 0 & 0 & 0 \\ 0 & 0 & 1 & 0 \\ 0 & 0 & 0 & -1 \end{bmatrix}$; $P = \begin{bmatrix} 1 & 0 & 0 & 0 \\ 0 & 1 & 0 & 0 \\ 0 & 0 & 1/\sqrt{2} & 1/\sqrt{2} \\ 0 & 0 & 1/\sqrt{2} & -1/\sqrt{2} \end{bmatrix}$.

12. $\begin{bmatrix} -3 & 0 & 0 \\ 0 & -3 & 0 \\ 0 & 0 & 3 \end{bmatrix}$; $P = \begin{bmatrix} -1/\sqrt{2} & -1/\sqrt{6} & 1/\sqrt{3} \\ 1/\sqrt{2} & -1/\sqrt{6} & 1/\sqrt{3} \\ 0 & 2/\sqrt{6} & 1/\sqrt{3} \end{bmatrix}$.

14. $\begin{bmatrix} 0 & 0 & 0 & 0 \\ 0 & 0 & 0 & 0 \\ 0 & 0 & 4 & 0 \\ 0 & 0 & 0 & 4 \end{bmatrix}$.

16. $\begin{bmatrix} 1 & 0 & 0 \\ 0 & 1 & 0 \\ 0 & 0 & 5 \end{bmatrix}$.

18. $\begin{bmatrix} 0 & 0 & 0 & 0 \\ 0 & 0 & 0 & 0 \\ 0 & 0 & 1 & 0 \\ 0 & 0 & 0 & -1 \end{bmatrix}$.

20. $\begin{bmatrix} -2 & 0 & 0 \\ 0 & -2 & 0 \\ 0 & 0 & -4 \end{bmatrix}$.

T.1. $(AX) \cdot Y = (AX)^T Y = X^T A^T Y = X \cdot (A^T Y).$

T.2. The i,j entry of the matrix product $A^T A$ represents the ith row of A^T times the jth column of A. That is, the dot product of the ith and jth columns of A. If $A^T A = I_n$, then the dot product of the ith and jth columns of A is 1 if i = j and 0 if $i \neq j$. Thus the columns of A form an orthonormal set in R^n. The converse is proved by reversing the steps in this argument.

T.3. If $A^T A = I_n$, $|A|^2 = |A^T| \cdot |A| = |A^T A| = |I_n| = 1$. Thus $|A| = \pm 1$.

T.4. As derived on p. 278, $L(X) \cdot L(Y) = X \cdot Y$ ("L preserves dot product"). Then $\|L(X)\| = \sqrt{L(X) \cdot L(X)} = \sqrt{X \cdot X} = \|X\|$. For nonzero vectors X and Y,

$$\cos(\text{∢ between } L(X) \text{ and } L(Y)) = \frac{L(X) \cdot L(Y)}{\|L(X)\| \cdot \|L(Y)\|} = \frac{X \cdot Y}{\|X\| \cdot \|Y\|}$$

$= \cos \theta$ where θ is the angle between X and Y.

T.5. Let $A = \begin{bmatrix} a & b \\ b & d \end{bmatrix}$ be a 2×2 symmetric matrix. Then its characteristic polynomial is $\lambda^2 - (a + d)\lambda + (ad - b^2)$. The roots of this polynomial are

$$\lambda = \frac{a+d \pm \sqrt{(a+d)^2 - 4(ad-b^2)}}{2}$$

$$= \frac{a+d \pm \sqrt{(a-d)^2 + 4b^2}}{2} .$$

If b = 0, A is already diagonal. If b ≠ 0, the discriminant $(a - d)^2 + 4b^2$ is positive and there are two distinct real eigenvalues. Thus A diagonalizable. By Theorem 5.2, there is a diagonalizing matrix P whose columns are linearly independent eigenvectors of A. We may assume further that those columns are unit vectors in R^2. By Theorem 5.5, the two columns are orthogonal. Thus P is an orthogonal matrix.

T.6. $(AB)^T(AB) = B^T A^T AB = B^T I_n B = I_n$.

T.7. $(A^{-1})^T A^{-1} = (A^T)^{-1} A^{-1} = (AA^T)^{-1} = I_n^{-1} = I_n$.

T.8. (a) $\begin{bmatrix} \cos\theta & -\sin\theta \\ \sin\theta & \cos\theta \end{bmatrix} \begin{bmatrix} \cos\theta & \sin\theta \\ -\sin\theta & \cos\theta \end{bmatrix} = I_2$,

(b) Let $A = \begin{bmatrix} a & b \\ c & d \end{bmatrix}$ be orthogonal. Then $A^T = \begin{bmatrix} a & c \\ b & d \end{bmatrix}$ is

orthogonal and its first column is a unit vector: $a^2 + b^2 = 1$. Let $a = \cos\theta$ and $b = \sin\theta$ for some θ. Then $0 = ac + bd = c\cos\theta + d\sin\theta$ implies $c = \mu\sin\theta$, $d = -\mu\cos\theta$ for some real number μ. But $1 = c^2 + d^2 = \mu^2(\sin^2\theta + \cos^2\theta) = \mu^2$ implies $\mu = \pm 1$.

T.9. For an n×n matrix A, if $A^T AY = Y = I_n Y$ for all Y in R^n, then $A^T A = I_n$. ($A^T A$ and I_n represent the same linear transformation, and with respect to a given basis, the matrix of a linear transformation is uniquely determined.)

Alternately, $(A^T A - I_n)Y = 0$ for all Y in R^n. Thus $A^T A - I_n$ is the zero matrix, so $A^T A = I_n$.

T.10. $\|X+Y\|^2 = (X+Y)\cdot(X+Y) = X\cdot X + 2X\cdot Y + Y\cdot Y = \|X\|^2 + 2(X\cdot Y) + \|Y\|^2$

thus $X\cdot Y = \frac{1}{2}(\|X+Y\|^2 - \|X\|^2 - \|Y\|^2)$. Then if L preserves length, $L(X)\cdot L(Y) = \frac{1}{2}(\|L(X)+L(Y)\|^2 - \|L(X)\|^2 - \|L(Y)\|^2)$
$= \frac{1}{2}(\|X+Y\|^2 - \|X\|^2 - \|Y\|^2) = X\cdot Y$.

Review Exercises, page 246

2. Not diagonalizable.

4. $P = \begin{bmatrix} 3 & 0 & 0 \\ -3 & 1 & 6 \\ 2 & 0 & 1 \end{bmatrix}$, $D = \begin{bmatrix} 1 & 0 & 0 \\ 0 & -1 & 0 \\ 0 & 0 & -2 \end{bmatrix}$

6. Not diagonalizable.

8. No.

10. $P = \begin{bmatrix} 2/\sqrt{5} & 0 & -1/\sqrt{5} \\ 0 & 1 & 0 \\ 1/\sqrt{5} & 0 & 2/\sqrt{5} \end{bmatrix}$, $D = \begin{bmatrix} -5 & 0 & 0 \\ 0 & 5 & 0 \\ 0 & 0 & 5 \end{bmatrix}$.

CHAPTER 6

Section 6.1, page 267

2. Maximize $z = 0.08x + 0.10y$

    subject to
    $$x + y \leq 6000$$
    $$x \geq 1500$$
    $$y \leq 4000$$
    $$x \geq 0, \ y \geq 0.$$

4. Maximize $z = 30x + 60y$

    subject to
    $$6x + 12y \leq 18,000$$
    $$3x + \ y \leq 1800$$
    $$x \geq 0, \ y \geq 0.$$

6. Minimize $z = 60x + 50y$

    subject to
    $$3x + 5y \leq 15$$
    $$4x + 4y \geq 16$$
    $$x \geq 0, \ y \geq 0.$$

8. Minimize $z = 20,000x + 25,000y$

    subject to
    $$40x + 60y \geq 300$$
    $$2x + \ 3y \leq \ 12$$
    $$x \geq 0, \ y \geq 0.$$

10.

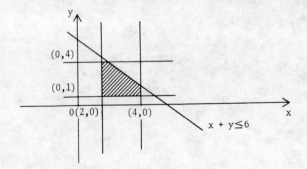

12.

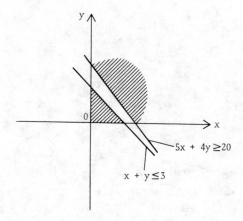

Labels on graph: $5x + 4y \geq 20$ and $x + y \leq 3$

14. $x = 18/5$, $y = 2/5$, optimal value of $z = 58/5$.

16. 3/2 tons of regular steel and 5/2 tons of special steel; maximum profit is $430.

18. Invest $4000 in bond A and $2000 in bond B; maximum return is $520.

20. Use 2 minutes of advertising and 28 minutes of programming; maximum number of viewer-minutes is 1,340,000.

22. Use 4 units of A and 3 units of B; maximum amount of protein is 34 units.

24. (b).

26. Maximize $z = 2x_1 - 3x_2 - 2x_3$

   subject to
   $$2x_1 + x_2 + 2x_3 \leq 12$$
   $$x_1 + x_2 - 3x_3 \leq 8$$
   $$x_1 \geq 0, \ x_2 \geq 0, \ x_3 \geq 0.$$

28. Maximize $z = 2x + 8y$

   subject to
   $$2x + 3y + u \qquad = 18$$
   $$3x - 2y \qquad + v = 6$$
   $$x \geq 0, \ y \geq 0, \ u \geq 0, \ v \geq 0.$$

2.

	x_1	x_2	x_3	x_4	x_5	z	
x_4	3	-2	1	1	0	0	4
x_5	2	4	5	0	1	0	6
	-2	-3	4	0	0	1	0

4.

	x_1	x_2	x_3	x_4	x_5	x_6	z	
x_4	1	-2	4	1	0	0	0	5
x_5	2	2	4	0	1	0	0	5
x_6	3	1	-1	0	0	1	0	7
	-2	3	-1	0	0	0	1	0

6. $x = 0$, $y = 6/7$, optimal $z = 30/7$.

8. No finite optimal solution.

10. $x_1 = 0$, $x_2 = 5/2$, $x_3 = 0$, optimal $z = 10$.

12. 3/2 tons of regular steel and 5/2 tons of special steel; maximum profit is $430.

14. 4 units of A and 3 units of B; maximum amount of protein is 34 units.

T.1. We must show that if X and Y are any two feasible solutions, then for any $0 \leq r \leq 1$, the vector $rX + (1-r)Y$ is also a feasible solution. First, since $r \geq 0$ and $(1-r) \geq 0$, and $AX \leq B$, $AY \leq B$,

$$A[rX + (1-r)Y] = rAX + (1-r)AY \leq rB + (1-r)B = B.$$

Also since $X \geq 0$, $Y \geq 0$,

$$rX + (1-r)Y \geq r \cdot 0 + (1-r) \cdot 0 = 0.$$

Thus $rX + (1-r)Y$ is a feasible solution.

T.2. Suppose that in a certain step of the simplex method, the minimum positive θ-ratio is not chosen.

After a reindexing of the variables, if necessary, we may assume that all the nonbasic variables occur first followed by all the basic variables. That is, we may assume that we start with the situation given by Tableau 2 on page 322. Let us further assume that x_1 is the entering variable and x_{n+1} the departing variable and that the θ-ratio b_2/a_{21} associated with the second row is positive and smaller than b_1/a_{11} associated with the first row -- the row of the incorrectly chosen departing variable x_{n+1}. Thus

$$0 < \frac{b_2}{a_{21}} < \frac{b_1}{a_{11}} ,$$

$$a_{11}b_2 < a_{21}b_1 ,$$

$$a_{11}b_2 - a_{21}b_1 < 0.$$

The new set of nonbasic variables is $\{x_2, \cdots, x_n, x_{n+1}\}$. Set these nonbasic variables equal to zero and solve the first equation for x_1:

$$a_{11}x_1 + a_{12} \cdot 0 + \cdots + a_{1n} \cdot 0 + 0 = b_1 ,$$

$$x_1 = b_1/a_{11}.$$

Next substitute this value for x_1 into the second equation and solve for the basic variable x_{n+2}:

$$a_{21} \left(\frac{b_1}{a_{11}} \right) + a_{22} \cdot 0 + \cdots + a_{2n} \cdot 0 + x_{n+2} = b_2 ,$$

$$x_{n+2} = b_2 - \frac{a_{21}b_1}{a_{11}} = \frac{a_{11}b_2 - a_{21}b_1}{a_{11}} = \frac{neg}{pos} = neg,$$

a contradiction to the fact that the coordinate x_{n+2} of any feasible solution must be ≥ 0.

2. Minimize $z' = 5w_1 + 6w_2$

    subject to
    $$w_1 + 2w_2 \geq 10$$
    $$3w_1 + 4w_2 \geq 12$$
    $$4w_1 - 5w_2 \geq 15$$

    $$w_1 \geq 0, \; w_2 \geq 0.$$

4. Maximize $z' = 9w_1 + 12w_2$

    subject to
    $$3w_1 + 5w_2 \leq 14$$
    $$5w_1 + 2w_2 \leq 12$$
    $$-4w_1 + 7w_2 \leq 18$$

    $$w_1 \geq 0, \; w_2 \geq 0.$$

6. $w_1 = 2/3$, $w_2 = 0$, optimal value = 4.

8. $w_1 = 1/10$, $w_2 = 7/10$, optimal value = 69/10.

10. Use 6 oz. of dates and no nuts or raisins. Total cost = 90¢.

2. Manufacture 100 units of model A and 500 units of model B daily. The maximum profit is $58,000.

4. Maximize $z' = 6y_1 + 10y_2$

    subject to

    $$2y_1 + 5y_2 \leq 6$$
    $$3y_1 + 2y_2 \leq 5$$

    $$y_1 \geq 0, \quad y_2 \geq 0.$$

Chapter 7

2. (a) $-x + y = 0$,   (b) $-x + 1 = 0$,

   (c) $y + 4 = 0$,   (d) $-x + y + 5 = 0$.

4. (c).

6. (a) $x = 2 + 2t$, $y = -3 + 5t$, $z = 1 + 4t$;

   (b) $x = -3 + 8t$, $y = -2 + 7t$, $z = -2 + 6t$;

   (c) $x = -2 + 4t$, $y = 3 - 6t$, $z = 4 + t$;

   (d) $x = 4t$, $y = 5t$, $z = 2t$.

8. (a), (d).

10. (a) $x - z + 2 = 0$;

   (b) $3x + y - 14z + 47 = 0$;

   (c) $-x - 10y + 7z = 0$;

   (d) $-4x - 19y + 14z + 9 = 0$.

12. (a) $-4y - z + 14 = 0$ and $4x - 3z + 2 = 0$;

   (b) $3y - 4z - 25 = 0$ and $3x + 2z + 2 = 0$;

   (c) $5x - 4y + 4 = 0$ and $x + 4z - 8 = 0$.

14. No.

16. (b).

18. $x = 3$, $y = -1 + t$, $z = -3 - 5t$.

20. $\left(\dfrac{-17}{5}, \dfrac{38}{5}, -6 \right)$.

22. $-2x + 4y - 5z - 27 = 0$.

24. $1/\sqrt{14}$

T.1. Since by hypothesis $a, b,$ and c are not all zero, take $a \neq 0$. Let $P_0 = (-d/a, 0, 0)$. Then from equations (8) 1 (9) on page 351, the equation of the plane through P_0 with normal vector $N = (a, b, c)$ is

$$a(x + \frac{d}{a}) + b(y-0) + c(z-0) = 0,$$

or

$$ax + by + cz + d = 0.$$

T.2. (a) L_1 and L_2 are parallel if and only if their direction vectors U and V are parallel, if and only if $U = aV$ for some scalar a.

(b) If L_1 and L_2 are identical, then they are parallel and so U and V are parallel. Also the point X_1 lies on line L_1 (L_1 and L_2 are the same line), so

$$X_1 = X_0 + sU$$

for some constant s. Thus $X_1 - X_0 = sU$, and $X_1 - X_0$ is parallel to U.

Conversely, if $X_1 - X_0$, U and V are mutually parallel, then the point X_1 lies on the line L_1, and so both L_1 and L_2 are lines through X_1 with the same direction and thus are identical lines.

(c) L_1 and L_2 are perpendicular if and only if their direction vectors U and V are perpendicular.

(d) If L_1 and L_2 intersect in a point X_3, then $X_3 = X_0 + sU = X_1 + tV$ for some s and t. Then $X_1 - X_0 = sU - tV$ is a linear combination of U and V. Reversing these steps proves the converse.

T.3. Possible solution: L_1: $x = s$, $y = z = 0$ (the x-axis) and
L_2: $x = 0$, $y = 1$, $z = t$.

T.4. By Exercise T.1, the coefficients of the first degree terms in an equation for a plane give a normal vector for that plane. Thus if $N_1 = (a_1, b_1, c_1)$ and $N_2 = (a_2, b_2, c_2)$ are two normal vectors for the same plane, N_1 and N_2 must be parallel, and so $N_2 = aN_1$ for some nonzero scalar a.

T.5. The whole space R^3, the zero subspace $\{0\}$, all lines through the origin, and all planes through the origin.

T.6. (a) Let $X_1 = (x_1, y_1, z_1)$ and $X_2 = (x_2, y_2, z_2)$ be points on the plane $ax + by + cz = 0$. Then

$$a(x_1+x_2) + b(y_1+y_2) + c(z_1+z_2)$$

$$= ax_1 + by_1 + cz_1 + ax_2 + by_2 + cz_2 = 0 + 0 = 0$$

and so $X_1 + X_2$ lies on the plane.

Also for any scalar r,

$$a(rx_1) + b(ry_1) + c(rz_1) = r(ax_1 + by_1 + cz_1)$$

$$= r \cdot 0 = 0$$

and so rX_1 lies on the plane.

(b) Possible solution: $\{(3,2,0), (-2,0,1)\}$.

T.7. Expand the determinant about the first row:

$$0 = \begin{vmatrix} x & y & z & 1 \\ a_1 & b_1 & c_1 & 1 \\ a_2 & b_2 & c_2 & 1 \\ a_3 & b_3 & c_3 & 1 \end{vmatrix} = xA_{11} + yA_{12} + zA_{13} + 1 \cdot A_{14} \qquad (*)$$

where A_{1j} is the cofactor of the $1, j$th element, and (being based on the second, third and fourth rows at the determinant) is a constant. (See (1) on page 93.) Thus (*) is an equation

of the form

$$ax + by + cz + d = 0$$

and so is the equation of some plane. The noncolinearity of the three points insures that the three cofactors A_{11}, A_{12}, A_{13} are not all zero.

Next let $(x,y,z) = (a_i, b_i, c_i)$. The determinant has two equal rows, and so has the value zero. Thus the point P_i lies on the plane whose equation is (*). Thus (*) is an equation for the plane through P_1, P_2, P_3.

2. (a) $[x_1 \; x_2 \; x_3] \begin{bmatrix} 1 & -2 & 0 \\ -2 & -3 & 3 \\ 0 & 3 & 4 \end{bmatrix} \begin{bmatrix} x_1 \\ x_2 \\ x_3 \end{bmatrix}$;

   (b) $[x \; y] \begin{bmatrix} 4 & -3 \\ -3 & 2 \end{bmatrix} \begin{bmatrix} x \\ y \end{bmatrix}$;

   (c) $[x_1 \; x_2 \; x_3] \begin{bmatrix} 0 & -1 & 2 \\ -1 & 0 & 3 \\ 2 & 3 & 0 \end{bmatrix} \begin{bmatrix} x_1 \\ x_2 \\ x_3 \end{bmatrix}$.

4. $3x'^2 - 2y'^2$.

6. $x_1'^2 - x_3'^2$.

8. $-2x_1'^2 + 5x_2'^2 - 5x_3'^2$.

10. $y_1^2 + y_2^2$.

12. $y_1^2 + y_2^2 + y_3^2$.

14. $y_1^2 - y_2^2$, a hyperbola.

16. $y_1^2 - y_2^2$, rank = 2, signature = 0.

18. (a) and (b) are positive definite. The eigenvalues of the
    matrices are: (a) 1, 3; (b) 1, 3; (c) 1, -1; (d) 0, 2;
    (e) 0, 4.

T.1. $(P^T A P)^T = P^T A^T P = P^T A P$ since $A^T = A$.

T.2. (a) $A = P^T A P$ for $P = I_n$.

(b) If $B = P^T A P$ with nonsingular P, then $A = (P^{-1})^T B P^{-1}$ and B is congruent to A.

(c) If $B = P^T A P$ and $C = Q^T B Q$ with P, Q nonsingular, then
$$C = Q^T P^T A P Q = (PQ)^T A (PQ) \text{ with } PQ \text{ nonsingular.}$$

T.3. By Theorem 5.7, for the symmetric matrix A, there exists an orthogonal matrix P such that

$$P^{-1} A P = D$$

is diagonal. Since P is orthogonal, $P^{-1} = P^T$. Thus A is congruent to D.

T.4. <u>Rank 2</u>: $y_1^2 + y_2^2$; $y_1^2 + y_2^2 = 1$ is a circle,

$y_1^2 - y_2^2$; $y_1^2 - y_2^2 = 1$ is a hyperbola,

$-y_1^2 - y_2^2$; $-y_1^2 - y_2^2 = 1$ is an imaginary conic (no real points).

<u>Rank 1</u>: y_1^2 ; $y_1^2 = 1$ is a pair of parallel lines,

$-y_1^2$; $-y_1^2 = 1$ has no real points.

<u>Rank 0</u>: 0 ; $0 = 1$ has no solutions.

T.5. See T.4 above.

T.6. Let $A = \begin{bmatrix} a & b \\ b & d \end{bmatrix}$ and let the eigenvalues of A be λ_1 and λ_2.

The characteristic polynomial of A is $f(\lambda) = \lambda^2 - (a + d)\lambda + ad - b^2$. If A is positive definite then both λ_1 and λ_2 are > 0, so $\lambda_1 \lambda_2 = |A| > 0$. Also, $\begin{bmatrix} 1 & 0 \end{bmatrix} \begin{bmatrix} a & b \\ c & d \end{bmatrix} \begin{bmatrix} 1 \\ 0 \end{bmatrix} = a > 0$.

Conversely, let $|A| > 0$ and $a > 0$. Then $\lambda_1 \lambda_2 = |A| > 0$ so λ_1 and λ_2 are of the same sign. If λ_1 and λ_2 are both < 0 then $\lambda_1 + \lambda_2 = a + d < 0$, so $d < -a$. Since $a > 0$, we have $d < 0$ and $ad < 0$. Now $|A| = ad - b^2 > 0$, which means that ad $> b^2$ so ad > 0, a contradiction. Hence, λ_1 and λ_2 are both positive.

T.7. Let A be positive definite and $g(X) = X^T A X$. By Theorem 7.2, $g(X)$ is a quadratic form which is equivalent to

$$h(Y) = y_1^2 + y_2^2 + \cdots + y_p^2 - y_{p+1}^2 - \cdots - y_r^2.$$ If g and h

are equivalent then $h(Y) > 0$ for each $Y \neq 0$. However, this can happen if and only if all terms in $h(Y)$ are positive; that is, if and only if A is congruent to I_n, or if and only if $A = P^T I_n P = P^T P$.

Section 7.3, page 329

2. (a)

	P_1	P_2	P_3	P_4	P_5
P_1	0	1	0	0	0
P_2	1	0	1	0	1
P_3	1	0	0	1	0
P_4	0	1	0	0	0
P_5	0	0	0	1	0

(b)

	P_1	P_2	P_3	P_4	P_5	P_6
P_1	0	1	1	0	0	0
P_2	1	0	0	1	0	0
P_3	0	1	0	0	0	0
P_4	0	0	1	0	1	1
P_5	0	0	1	1	0	1
P_6	1	0	0	0	0	0

4. (a)

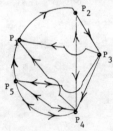

(b)

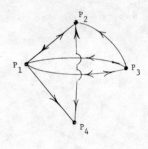

6.

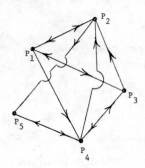

	P_1	P_2	P_3	P_4	P_5
P_1	0	1	1	1	0
P_2	1	0	0	0	1
P_3	1	1	0	1	0
P_4	0	1	1	0	1
P_5	0	0	0	1	0

8. (a) Peters;
    (b) Russell.

10. (a) No;
    (b) 3;
    (c) 5.

12. P_1, P_4, P_5, and P_6.

14. (a) No;
    (b) 3;
    (c) 4.

16. (a) Strongly connected;   (b) Not strongly connected.

T.1. In a dominance digraph, for each i and j, it is not the case
     that both P_i dominates P_j and P_j dominates P_i.

T.2. Let r=2. For each i and j, $b_{ij}^{(2)}$, the number of ways P_i
     has two-stage access to P_j, is the number of indices k,
     $1 \le k \le n$, such that P_i has direct access to P_k and P_k
     has direct access to P_j. This in turn is the number of k
     such that $a_{ik} = 1$ and $a_{kj} = 1$ where $A(G) = [a_{ij}]$, which is

$$\sum_{k=1}^{n} a_{ik} a_{kj} = \text{i,j entry of } [A(G)]^2.$$

     For r>2, assume that the theorem has been proved for
     values up to r-1. Then

     $b_{ij}^{(r)}$ = the number of k such that P_i has r-1 stage
     access to P_k and P_k has direct access to P_j,

$$= \sum_{k=1}^{n} b_{ik}^{(r-1)} \cdot a_{kj} = \sum_{k=1}^{n} (i,k \text{ entry of } [A(G)]^{r-1}) \cdot k,j$$

entry of $A(G) = i,j$ entry of $[A(G)]^r$.

T.3. The implication in one direction is proved on p. 383. Next suppose P_i belongs to the clique $\{P_i, P_j, P_k, \cdots, P_m\}$. According to the definition of clique, it contains at least three vertices so we may assume P_i, P_j and P_k all exist in the clique. Then $s_{ij} = s_{ji} = s_{jk} = s_{kj} = s_{ik} = s_{ki} = 1$ and $s_{ii}^{(3)}$ is a sum of nonnegative integer terms including the positive term which represents three stage access from P_i to P_j to P_k to P_i. Thus $s_{ii}^{(3)}$ is positive.

Section 7.4, page 346

2.

		C	
	stone	scissors	paper
stone	0	1	-1
R scissors	-1	0	1
paper	1	-1	0

4.

		C's guess	
		Nickel	Dime
R's Nickel		-5	5
Choice Dime		10	-10

6. (a) $P = [0 \quad 1]$, $Q = \begin{bmatrix} 1 \\ 0 \end{bmatrix}$, $v = 3$;

(b) $P = [0 \quad 1 \quad 0]$, $Q = \begin{bmatrix} 0 \\ 1 \\ 0 \end{bmatrix}$, $v = -1$;

(c) $P = [0 \quad 1 \quad 0 \quad 0]$, $Q = \begin{bmatrix} 0 \\ 0 \\ 1 \\ 0 \end{bmatrix}$, $v = -2$

or

$$P = [1 \quad 0 \quad 0 \quad 0], \quad Q = \begin{bmatrix} 0 \\ 0 \\ 1 \\ 0 \end{bmatrix}, \quad v = -2.$$

8. (a) 5/3; (b) 1/12.

10. $p_1 = 2/3$, $p_2 = 1/3$, $q_1 = 5/6$, $q_2 = 1/6$, $v = 14/3$.

12. $p_1 = 0$, $p_2 = 3/4$, $p_3 = 1/4$, $q_1 = 3/4$, $q_2 = 1/4$, $v = 29/4$.

14. $P = [3/7 \quad 0 \quad 4/7]$, $Q = \begin{bmatrix} 2/7 \\ 5/7 \\ 0 \end{bmatrix}$, $v = -1/7$.

16. $P = [11/20 \quad 9/20]$, $Q = \begin{bmatrix} 11/20 \\ 9/20 \end{bmatrix}$, $v = 1/20$.

18. $P = [1 \quad 0]$, $Q = \begin{bmatrix} 1 \\ 0 \end{bmatrix}$, $v = 50$.

20. For labor: $p_1 = 2/3$, $p_2 = 0$, $p_3 = 1/3$;

for management: $q_1 = 1/2$, $q_2 = 1/2$, $v = 3$ million.

T.1. The expected payoff to R is the sum of terms of the form

(Probability that R plays row i and C plays column j)

$\times$ (Payoff to R when R plays i and C plays j) $= p_i q_j a_{ij}$.

Summing over all $1 \leq i \leq m$ and $1 \leq j \leq n$, we get

$$\text{Expected payoff to } R = \sum_{i=1}^{m} \sum_{j=1}^{n} p_i a_{ij} q_j = PAQ.$$

T.2. Let P_0 be an optimal strategy for R for the original game with payoff matrix $A = [a_{ij}]$. Then for any strategy Q for C and any strategy P for R

$$E(P_0, Q) = P_0 A Q \geq PAQ = E(P, Q) ,$$

or

$$\sum_{i=1}^{m} \sum_{j=1}^{n} p_i^{(0)} a_{ij} q_j \geq \sum_{i=1}^{m} \sum_{j=1}^{n} p_i a_{ij} q_j ,$$

where $P_0 = (p_i^{(0)})$, $P = (p_i)$, and $Q = [q_j]$.

Let $A' = [a_{ij}+r]$ be the payoff matrix for the new game in which each payoff to R has been increased by the constant r. Let E' be the expected payoff to R for the new game. Then

$$E'(P,Q) = \sum_{i=1}^{m} \sum_{j=1}^{n} P_i (a_{ij}+r) q_j$$

$$= \sum_{i=1}^{m} \sum_{j=1}^{n} P_i a_{ij} q_j + \sum_{i=1}^{m} \sum_{j=1}^{n} P_i r q_j = E(P,Q) + r \left(\sum_{i=1}^{m} P_i\right)\left(\sum_{j=1}^{n} q_j\right)$$

$$= E(P,Q) + r.$$

Likewise $E'(P_0,Q) = E(P_0,Q) + r$.

Then,

$$E'(P_0,Q) = E(P_0,Q) + r \geq E(P,Q) + r = E'(P,Q)$$

and so P_0 is also an optimal strategy for R for the new game.

Similarly the optimal strategy Q_0 for C is the same for both the original game and the new game.

Finally the value v' of the new game is

$$E'(P_0,Q_0) = E(P_0,Q_0) + r = v + r$$

where v is the value of the original game.

2. $y = 0.3x + 1.3$.

4. $y = 0.321x + 2.786$.

6. (a) $y = 0.697x + 1.457$; (b) 7.73 .

T.1.

$$A^T A = \begin{bmatrix} 1 & 1 & \cdots & 1 \\ x_1 & x_2 & \cdots & x_n \end{bmatrix} \begin{bmatrix} 1 & x_1 \\ 1 & x_2 \\ \cdot & \cdot \\ \cdot & \cdot \\ \cdot & \cdot \\ 1 & x_n \end{bmatrix} = \begin{bmatrix} n & \sum x_i \\ \sum x_i & \sum x_i^2 \end{bmatrix} ,$$

$$A^T Y = \begin{bmatrix} 1 & 1 & \cdots & 1 \\ x_1 & x_2 & \cdots & x_n \end{bmatrix} \begin{bmatrix} y_1 \\ y_2 \\ \cdot \\ \cdot \\ y_n \end{bmatrix} = \begin{bmatrix} \sum y_i \\ \sum x_i y_i \end{bmatrix} ,$$

Thus (7) is $\begin{bmatrix} n & \sum x_i \\ \sum x_i & \sum x_i^2 \end{bmatrix} \begin{bmatrix} b_0 \\ b_1 \end{bmatrix} = \begin{bmatrix} \sum y_i \\ \sum x_i y_i \end{bmatrix}$,

which gives (5).

T.2.   Suppose all x coordinates x_i equal a common value x_1.

Then $A^T A$ becomes $\begin{bmatrix} n & nx_1 \\ nx_1 & nx_1^2 \end{bmatrix}$, which is singular. (The

second row is x_1 times the first row).

Section 7.6, page 363

2. $\begin{bmatrix} 3 \\ 3 \\ 8 \end{bmatrix}$.

4. $\begin{bmatrix} 15 \\ 3 \\ 14 \end{bmatrix}$.

6. C_1's income is 24; C_2's income is 25, C_3's income is 16.

8. Productive

10. Productive

12. $2.805 million of copper, $2.125 million of transportation, $4.158 million of electric power.

T.1. We must show that for an exchange matrix A and vector P,

AP $\leq$ P implies AP = P.

Let A = $[a_{ij}]$, P = $[p_j]$ and AP = Y = $[y_j]$.

Then

$$\sum_{j=1}^{n} y_j = \sum_{j=1}^{n} \sum_{k=1}^{n} a_{jk} p_k = \sum_{k=1}^{n} \left(\sum_{j=1}^{n} a_{jk} \right) p_k = \sum_{k=1}^{n} p_k$$

since the sum of the entries in the kth column of A is 1.

Since $y_j \leq p_j$ for j = 1,$\cdots$,n and $\sum y_j = \sum p_j$,

the respective entries must be equal: $y_j = p_j$ for

j = 1,$\cdots$,n. Thus AP = P.

Section 7.7, page 373

2. (b) and (c).

4. (a)

$$p^{(1)} = \begin{bmatrix} 0.2 \\ 0.3 \\ 0.5 \end{bmatrix}, \quad p^{(2)} = \begin{bmatrix} 0.06 \\ 0.24 \\ 0.70 \end{bmatrix}, \quad p^{(3)} = \begin{bmatrix} 0.048 \\ 0.282 \\ 0.670 \end{bmatrix}, \quad p^{(4)} = \begin{bmatrix} 0.056 \\ 0.286 \\ 0.658 \end{bmatrix} ;$$

(b) Let * stand for any positive matrix entry. Then

$$T^2 = \begin{bmatrix} 0 & * & 0 \\ 0 & * & * \\ * & * & * \end{bmatrix} \cdot \begin{bmatrix} 0 & * & 0 \\ 0 & * & * \\ * & * & * \end{bmatrix} = \begin{bmatrix} 0 & * & * \\ * & * & * \\ * & * & * \end{bmatrix},$$

$$T^3 = T^2 \cdot T = \begin{bmatrix} 0 & * & * \\ * & * & * \\ * & * & * \end{bmatrix} \cdot \begin{bmatrix} 0 & * & 0 \\ 0 & * & * \\ * & * & * \end{bmatrix} = \begin{bmatrix} * & * & * \\ * & * & * \\ * & * & * \end{bmatrix} > 0,$$

hence T is regular. $U = \begin{bmatrix} 0.057 \\ 0.283 \\ 0.660 \end{bmatrix}$.

6. In general, each matrix is regular and so T^n converges to a state of equilibrium.

Specifically, $T^n \rightarrow$ a matrix all of whose columns are U
where:

(a)
$$U = \begin{bmatrix} 2/3 \\ 1/3 \end{bmatrix},$$

(b)
$$U = \begin{bmatrix} 1/4 \\ 3/4 \end{bmatrix},$$

(c)
$$U = \begin{bmatrix} 9/17 \\ 4/17 \\ 4/17 \end{bmatrix},$$

(d)
$$U = \begin{bmatrix} 0.333 \\ 0.111 \\ 0.555 \end{bmatrix}.$$

8. (a) $\begin{bmatrix} 3/7 \\ 4/7 \end{bmatrix}$, (b) $\begin{bmatrix} 1/8 \\ 7/8 \end{bmatrix}$, (c) $\begin{bmatrix} 4/11 \\ 4/11 \\ 3/11 \end{bmatrix}$, (d) $\begin{bmatrix} 1/11 \\ 4/11 \\ 6/11 \end{bmatrix}$.

10. (a)
$$T = \begin{bmatrix} 0.6 & 0.25 \\ 0.4 & 0.75 \end{bmatrix};$$

(b)
$$T \begin{bmatrix} 0.4 \\ 0.6 \end{bmatrix} = \begin{bmatrix} 0.39 \\ 0.61 \end{bmatrix};$$

39% will order a subscription.

12. red, 25%; pink, 50%; white, 25%.

Section 7.8, page 379

2. $A^k = (PBP^{-1})(PBP^{-1}) \cdots (PBP^{-1})$

$= PB(P^{-1}P)B(P^{-1}P) \cdots (P^{-1}P)BP^{-1}$

$= PB^k P^{-1}$.

4. (a) $u_0 = u_1 = 1$, $u_n = u_{n-1} + 2u_{n-2}$ for $n \geq 2$;

(b)
$$A = \begin{bmatrix} 1 & 2 \\ 1 & 0 \end{bmatrix}, \quad U_{n-1} = A^{n-1}U_0,$$ A is similar to the diagonal

matrix $D = \begin{bmatrix} 2 & 0 \\ 0 & -1 \end{bmatrix}$, $u_n = \frac{1}{3}\left[2^{n+1} + (-1)^n\right]$.

T.1. Let us define u_{-1} to be 0. Then for n=0,

$$A^1 = A = \begin{bmatrix} 1 & 1 \\ 1 & 0 \end{bmatrix} = \begin{bmatrix} u_1 & u_0 \\ u_0 & u_{-1} \end{bmatrix},$$

for n=1, $\quad A^2 = \begin{bmatrix} 2 & 1 \\ 1 & 1 \end{bmatrix} = \begin{bmatrix} u_2 & u_1 \\ u_1 & u_0 \end{bmatrix}.$

Suppose inductively that the formula

$$A^{n+1} = \begin{bmatrix} u_{n+1} & u_n \\ u_n & u_{n-1} \end{bmatrix} \qquad (*)$$

holds for values up to and including n, $n \geq 1$. Then

$$A^{n+2} = A \cdot A^{n+1} = \begin{bmatrix} 1 & 1 \\ 1 & 0 \end{bmatrix} \begin{bmatrix} u_{n+1} & u_n \\ u_n & u_{n-1} \end{bmatrix}$$

$$= \begin{bmatrix} u_{n+1} + u_n & u_n + u_{n-1} \\ u_{n+1} & u_n \end{bmatrix} = \begin{bmatrix} u_{n+2} & u_{n+1} \\ u_{n+1} & u_n \end{bmatrix}.$$

Thus the formula (*) also holds for n+1. By mathematical induction, it holds for all natural numbers n.

Using (*), we see that

$$u_{n+1}u_{n-1} - u_n^2 = \begin{vmatrix} u_{n+1} & u_n \\ u_n & u_{n-1} \end{vmatrix} = \left| A^{n+1} \right| = |A|^{n+1} = (-1)^{n+1}.$$

2. (a) $X(t) = b_1 \begin{bmatrix} 1 \\ 0 \\ 0 \end{bmatrix} e^t + b_2 \begin{bmatrix} 0 \\ 1 \\ 0 \end{bmatrix} e^{-2t} + b_3 \begin{bmatrix} 0 \\ 1 \\ 5 \end{bmatrix} e^{3t}.$

    (b) $X(t) = 2 \begin{bmatrix} 1 \\ 0 \\ 0 \end{bmatrix} e^t + 3 \begin{bmatrix} 0 \\ 1 \\ 0 \end{bmatrix} e^{-2t} + 4 \begin{bmatrix} 0 \\ 1 \\ 5 \end{bmatrix} e^{3t}.$

4.

$X(t) = b_1 \begin{bmatrix} 1 \\ 0 \\ 0 \end{bmatrix} e^{2t} + b_2 \begin{bmatrix} 0 \\ 0 \\ 1 \end{bmatrix} e^{2t} + b_3 \begin{bmatrix} -3 \\ 1 \\ 0 \end{bmatrix} e^{t}.$

6.

$X(t) = b_1 \begin{bmatrix} 1 \\ -1 \end{bmatrix} e^{5t} + b_2 \begin{bmatrix} 1 \\ 1 \end{bmatrix} e^{t}.$

8.

$X(t) = b_1 \begin{bmatrix} 0 \\ -2 \\ 1 \end{bmatrix} e^{t} + b_2 \begin{bmatrix} 1 \\ 0 \\ 0 \end{bmatrix} e^{t} + b_3 \begin{bmatrix} 1 \\ 0 \\ 1 \end{bmatrix} e^{3t}.$

T.1. Let X_1 and X_2 be solutions to the equation $X' = AX$, and let a and b be scalars. Then

$$\frac{d}{dt}(aX_1 + bX_2) = aX_1' + bX_2' = aAX_1 + bAX_2 = A(aX_1 + bX_2)$$

Thus $aX_1 + bX_2$ is also a solution to the given equation.

Review Exercises, page 392

2. $x = -\frac{5}{3} - \frac{5}{3}t$, $y = \frac{2}{3} - \frac{1}{3}t$, $-\infty < t < \infty$.

4. 2

6. $y = -\frac{15}{68} + \frac{19}{17}x$

8. (a) $\begin{bmatrix} 0.2 & 0.6 \\ 0.8 & 0.4 \end{bmatrix}$;   (b) 0.4432 ;   (c) $\frac{3}{7}$.

10. (a) $X = b_1 \begin{bmatrix} 1 \\ 1 \end{bmatrix} e^{2t} + b_2 \begin{bmatrix} -1 \\ 3 \end{bmatrix} e^{-2t}$;

    (b) $X = \frac{9}{2} \begin{bmatrix} 1 \\ 1 \end{bmatrix} e^{2t} + \frac{1}{2} \begin{bmatrix} -1 \\ 3 \end{bmatrix} e^{-2t}$.

CHAPTER 8

Section 8.1, page 399

2. -0.2135×10^{-3} .

4. 0.2400×10^2 .

6. -0.4257×10^1, -0.4256×10^1.

8. 0.2167×10^1, 0.2166×10^1.

10. $\varepsilon_a = 0.606 \times 10^{-1}$, $\varepsilon_r = -0.126$.

12. $\varepsilon_a = 0.18 \times 10^{-3}$, $\varepsilon_r = 0.25 \times 10^{-1}$.

2. $\begin{bmatrix} 1 & 3/2 & 2 & 5/2 \\ 0 & 1 & -2 & -3 \\ 0 & 0 & 1 & 2 \\ 0 & 0 & 0 & 1 \end{bmatrix}$.

4. $x_1 = 11/5$, $x_2 = -28/45$, $x_3 = 53/30$.

6. $x_1 \simeq 2.999$, $x_2 \simeq -2.000$, $x_3 \simeq 5.002$.

8. $x_1 \simeq -5.521$, $x_2 \simeq 3.205$, $x_3 \simeq 4.222$.

10. (a) and (d).

12.

	Jacobi	Gauss-Seidel	Exact
x_1	2.919	2.988	3
x_2	-1.867	-1.990	-2
x_3	4.027	4.003	4

14.

	Jacobi	Gauss-Seidel	Exact
x_1	-0.398	-0.399	-2/5
x_2	0.505	0.501	1/2
x_3	-3.006	-3.000	-3

Section 8.3, page 418

	Approximate			Exact	
	Eigenvalue	Eigenvector		Eigenvalue	Eigenvector
2.	2.029	$[-0.488 \quad 1]^T$		2	$[-1/2 \quad 1]^T$
4.	4.948	$[1 \quad -0.511]^T$		5	$[1 \quad -1/2]^T$
6.	5.998	$[0.707 \quad 0.707]^T$		6	$[1/\sqrt{2} \quad 1/\sqrt{2}]^T$
	-2.000	$[-0.707 \quad 0.707]^T$		-2	$[-1/\sqrt{2} \quad 1/\sqrt{2}]^T$

	Approximate		Exact	
	Eigenvalue	Eigenvector	Eigen-value	Eigenvector
8.	8.988	$[0.666 \quad -0.333 \quad -0.666]^T$	9	$[2/3 \quad -1/3 \quad -2/3]^T$
	-8.990	$[0.235 \quad 0.942 \quad -0.235]^T$	-9	$[1/2\sqrt{3} \quad 2/\sqrt{3} \quad -1/2\sqrt{3}]^T$
	-8.998	$[0.707 \quad 0 \quad 0.707]^T$	-9	$[1/\sqrt{2} \quad 0 \quad 1/\sqrt{2}]^T$

T.1.

$$E_{pq}E_{pq}^T = \begin{bmatrix} 1 & & & & \\ & \ddots & & & \\ & & \cos\theta & \sin\theta & \\ & & -\sin\theta & \cos\theta & \\ & & & & \ddots \\ & & & & & 1 \end{bmatrix} \begin{bmatrix} 1 & & & & \\ & \ddots & & & \\ & & \cos\theta & -\sin\theta & \\ & & \sin\theta & \cos\theta & \\ & & & & \ddots \\ & & & & & 1 \end{bmatrix}$$

$$= \begin{bmatrix} 1 & & & & \\ & \ddots & & & \\ & & \cos^2\theta + \sin^2\theta & 0 & \\ & & 0 & \cos^2\theta + \sin^2\theta & \\ & & & & \ddots \\ & & & & & 1 \end{bmatrix} = I_n .$$

Review Exercises, page 418

	Approximate		Exact	
	Eigenvalue	Eigenvector	Eigenvalue	Eigenvector
2.	2.036	$[1 \quad -0.828]^T$	2	$[-6 \quad 5]^T$